AAT

Final Accounts Preparation

Level 3

Advanced Diploma in Accounting

Question Bank

For assessments from September 2017

Third edition 2017

ISBN 9781 5097 1258 8

British Library Cataloguing-in-Publication Data

A catalogue record for this book is available from the British Library

Published by

BPP Learning Media Ltd
BPP House, Aldine Place
142-144 Uxbridge Road
London W12 8AA

www.bpp.com/learningmedia

Printed in the United Kingdom

Your learning materials, published by BPP Learning Media Ltd, are printed on paper obtained from traceable sustainable sources.

Contents

Introduction

This is BPP Learning Media's AAT Question Bank for *Final Accounts Preparation*. It is part of a suite of ground-breaking resources produced by BPP Learning Media for AAT assessments.

This Question Bank has been written in conjunction with the BPP Course Book, and has been carefully designed to enable students to practise all of the learning outcomes and assessment criteria for the units that make up *Final Accounts Preparation*. It is fully up to date as at June 2017 and reflects both the AAT's qualification specification and the sample assessment provided by the AAT.

This Question Bank contains these key features:

- Tasks corresponding to each chapter of the Course Book. Some tasks are designed for learning purposes, others are of assessment standard

- AAT's AQ2016 sample assessment 1 and answers for *Final Accounts Preparation* and further BPP practice assessments

The emphasis in all tasks and assessments is on the practical application of the skills acquired.

VAT

You may find tasks throughout this Question Bank that need you to calculate or be aware of a rate of VAT. This is stated at 20% in these examples and questions.

Approaching the assessment

When you sit the assessment it is very important that you follow the on screen instructions. This means you need to carefully read the instructions, both on the introduction screens and during specific tasks.

When you access the assessment you should be presented with an introductory screen with information similar to that shown below (taken from the introductory screen from one of the AAT's AQ2016 sample assessments for *Final Accounts Preparation*).

We have provided this **sample assessment** to help you familiarise yourself with our e-assessment environment. It is designed to demonstrate as many as possible of the question types that you may find in a live assessment. It is not designed to be used on its own to determine whether you are ready for a live assessment.

Assessment information:

You have **2 hours** to complete this sample assessment.

This assessment contains **6 tasks** and you should attempt to complete **every** task.
Each task is independent. You will not need to refer to your answers to previous tasks.
Read every task carefully to make sure you understand what is required.

The standard rate of VAT is 20%.

Where the date is relevant, it is given in the task data.
Both minus signs and brackets can be used to indicate negative numbers **unless** task instructions say otherwise.

You must use a full stop to indicate a decimal point. For example, write 100.57 NOT 100,57 or 100 57
You may use a comma to indicate a number in the thousands, but you don't have to. For example 10000 and 10,000 are both acceptable.

The actual instructions will vary depending on the subject you are studying for. It is very important you read the instructions on the introductory screen and apply them in the assessment. You don't want to lose marks when you know the correct answer just because you have not entered it in the right format.

In general, the rules set out in the AAT sample assessments for the subject you are studying for will apply in the real assessment, but you should carefully read the information on this screen again in the real assessment, just to make sure. This screen may also confirm the VAT rate used if applicable.

A full stop is needed to indicate a decimal point. We would recommend using minus signs to indicate negative numbers and leaving out the comma signs to indicate thousands, as this results in a lower number of key strokes and less margin for error when working under time pressure. Having said that, you can use whatever is easiest for you as long as you operate within the rules set out for your particular assessment.

You have to show competence throughout the assessment and you should therefore complete all of the tasks. Don't leave questions unanswered.

In some assessments, written or complex tasks may be human marked. In this case you are given a blank space or table to enter your answer into. You are told in the assessments which tasks these are (note: there may be none if all answers are marked by the computer).

If these involve calculations, it is a good idea to decide in advance how you are going to lay out your answers to such tasks by practising answering them on a word document, and certainly you should try all such tasks in this Question Bank and in the AAT's environment using the sample assessment.

When asked to fill in tables, or gaps, never leave any blank even if you are unsure of the answer. Fill in your best estimate.

Note that for some assessments where there is a lot of scenario information or tables of data provided (eg tax tables), you may need to access these via 'pop-ups'. Instructions will be provided on how you can bring up the necessary data during the assessment.

Finally, take note of any task specific instructions once you are in the assessment. For example you may be asked to enter a date in a certain format or to enter a number to a certain number of decimal places.

Grading

To achieve the qualification and to be awarded a grade, you must pass all the mandatory unit assessments, all optional unit assessments (where applicable) and the synoptic assessment.

The AAT Level 3 Advanced Diploma in Accounting will be awarded a grade. This grade will be based on performance across the qualification. Unit assessments and synoptic assessments are not individually graded. These assessments are given a mark that is used in calculating the overall grade.

How overall grade is determined

You will be awarded an overall qualification grade (Distinction, Merit, and Pass). If you do not achieve the qualification you will not receive a qualification certificate, and the grade will be shown as unclassified.

The marks of each assessment will be converted into a percentage mark and rounded up or down to the nearest whole number. This percentage mark is then weighted according to the weighting of the unit assessment or synoptic assessment within the qualification. The resulting weighted assessment percentages are combined to arrive at a percentage mark for the whole qualification.

Grade definition	Percentage threshold
Distinction	90–100%
Merit	80–89%
Pass	70–79%
Unclassified	0–69%
	Or failure to pass one or more assessment/s

Re-sits

Some AAT qualifications such as the AAT Advanced Diploma in Accounting have restrictions in place for how many times you are able to re-sit assessments. Please refer to the AAT website for further details.

You should only be entered for an assessment when you are well prepared and you expect to pass the assessment.

AAT qualifications

The material in this book may support the following AAT qualifications:

AAT Advanced Diploma in Accounting Level 3, AAT Advanced Diploma in Accounting at SCQF Level 6 and Further Education and Training Certificate: Accounting Technician (Level 4 AATSA)

Supplements

From time to time we may need to publish supplementary materials to one of our titles. This can be for a variety of reasons. From a small change in the AAT unit guidance to new legislation coming into effect between editions.

You should check our supplements page regularly for anything that may affect your learning materials. All supplements are available free of charge on our supplements page on our website at:

www.bpp.com/learning-media/about/students

Improving material and removing errors

There is a constant need to update and enhance our study materials in line with both regulatory changes and new insights into the assessments.

From our team of authors BPP appoints a subject expert to update and improve these materials for each new edition.

Their updated draft is subsequently technically checked by another author and from time to time non-technically checked by a proof reader.

We are very keen to remove as many numerical errors and narrative typos as we can but given the volume of detailed information being changed in a short space of time we know that a few errors will sometimes get through our net.

We apologise in advance for any inconvenience that an error might cause. We continue to look for new ways to improve these study materials and would welcome your suggestions. If you have any comments about this book, please email nisarahmed@bpp.com or write to Nisar Ahmed, AAT Head of Programme, BPP Learning Media Ltd, BPP House, Aldine Place, London W12 8AA.

Question Bank

Chapter 1 – Organisations and their final accounts

Task 1.1

Identify the type of organisation being described.

Description	Type of organisation
A business that is a separate legal entity from its owners; the owners have shares in the business.	▼
An organisation that meets the definition of a charity as set out in the Charities Act 2011. It is established for charitable purposes only.	▼
An unincorporated business owned and managed by two or more people.	▼
An unincorporated business owned and managed by one person.	▼
A business that is a separate legal entity owned and managed by two or more people.	▼

Picklist:

Charity
Limited company
Limited liability partnership
Partnership (unincorporated)
Sole trader

Task 1.2

Complete the following definition of unincorporated businesses.

Sole traders and partnerships are [(1) ▼]. This means there is [(2) ▼] between the business and their owners. Consequently sole traders and partners have [(3) ▼] for the business's obligations.

Picklist (1):

incorporated businesses
unincorporated businesses

Picklist (2):

a legal distinction
no legal distinction

Picklist (3):

limited liability
unlimited liability

Task 1.3

Which ONE option from the list below is a benefit of running a business as a sole trader?

Options	✓
In the event that the business generates a loss, this is shared by the partners instead of being borne by a sole trader only.	
Any debts of the business that cannot be met from the business assets are met from the owners' private resources.	
In the event that the business generates a profit, this is due to the sole trader only.	
The sole trader is not liable for the debts of the business.	

Task 1.4

Which ONE of the list below is a benefit of incorporation?

Options	✓
The company's shareholders are not personally liable for the debts of the business.	
The company directors must ensure the accounts are filed at Companies House by a specified date.	
Companies must comply with the provisions of the Companies Act whereas unincorporated businesses do not.	
The company's tax charge must be shown in the statement of profit or loss.	

Task 1.5

Complete the following sentences.

Statement	Answer
When a sole trader takes money from the business for personal use, this is known as	▼
In addition to a salary, a director (who is also a shareholder) of a limited liability company may be paid a	▼

Picklist:

capital
dividend
drawings
salary

Task 1.6

Which type of organisation will show a tax charge (or credit) in the statement of profit or loss? Select ONE organisation only.

Type of organisation	✓
Sole trader	
Partnership (unincorporated)	
Limited liability partnership	
Limited company	
Charity	

Task 1.7

Match the type of organisation with an appropriate description of the organisation's tax position.

Description of the organisation's tax position	Type of organisation(s)
Organisations that meet the definition of a charity and that are registered with the Charities Commission do not pay tax on most types of income.	▼
Tax will not be classed as a business expense in the statement of profit or loss; each partner must prepare a self-assessment tax return.	▼
Tax will not be classed as a business expense in the statement of profit or loss; the owner of the business must prepare a self-assessment tax return.	▼

Picklist:

Charity
Limited company
Limited liability partnership and Partnership (unincorporated)
Sole trader

Task 1.8

You work for a firm of accountants and are preparing the accounts for a sole trader.

The owner of the business is concerned that profits will be lower than expected. This could affect his ability to obtain a bank loan in the next financial year.

The owner asks you to change the depreciation policy so that the charge is lower in the final accounts this year, in comparison to the prior year.

What should you do? Choose ONE.

Action	✓
Obey the owner as it is his company.	
Explain that accounting policies have to reflect the most appropriate accounting treatment and that they cannot be changed simply to improve reported profit.	
Report the owner to the police.	

Task 1.9

You work for a firm of accountants and are preparing the final accounts for a client.

You are about to take a long train journey and a colleague suggests this is a suitable time to work on your clients' accounts.

What should you do? Choose ONE.

Action	✓
Agree that this is a sensible course of action.	
Explain that the information provided by your client is confidential and that you cannot risk sensitive information being seen by a member of the public.	

Task 1.10

You are a trainee working for a firm of accountants and are preparing the final accounts for a new client.

You see that inventory is a material figure in the client's accounting records. However, you are unfamiliar with IAS 2 *Inventories* and do not know the detailed accounting treatment of this item.

What should you do? Choose ONE.

Action	✓
Email the client explaining that your firm must decline the engagement.	
Attempt to prepare the accounts yourself, including the inventories figure.	
Speak to your manager and request support in this assignment.	

Task 1.11

You have worked as a qualified accountant for many years. Recently you joined a local firm of accountants and are asked to prepare the final accounts for Sandbury Trading. Your uncle owns Sandbury Trading.

What is the main risk that arises if you prepare the accounts for Sandbury Trading? Choose ONE.

Risks	✓
Objectivity is a risk here. Your uncle owns Sandbury Trading. If you prepare the accounts for this organisation, it could be perceived that you may be biased towards presenting financial information in your uncle's favour.	
Confidentiality is a risk as you will need Sandbury Trading's financial information in order to prepare the final accounts.	
Professional competence and due care is a risk as it seems that you are not qualified to prepare the final accounts.	

Chapter 2 - Incomplete records

Task 2.1

Why may information be missing from the accounting records? Select TWO options.

Options	✓
It appears in the statement of profit or loss only.	
There was an issue with the IT system and backups had not been kept.	
An employee failed to record certain transactions.	
An error was made when posting the depreciation charge for the year.	

Task 2.2

Why may the total of the sales ledger balances be higher than the balance on the sales ledger control account? Select ONE option.

Options	✓
The totals of the sales day book were overstated.	
Payments made to credit suppliers were omitted from the suppliers' accounts in the purchases ledger.	
Invoices sent to credit customers were duplicated in the sales ledger.	
Bank receipts from credit customers were duplicated in the sales ledger.	

Task 2.3

When preparing final accounts, from the options below, what type of financial information is most likely to be missing from the accounting records? Select ONE option.

Options	✓
Invoices sent to customers in respect of credit sales	
Invoice received from suppliers in respect of credit purchases	
Capital contributions from the owner into the business bank account	
Sundry expenses paid from petty cash	

Task 2.4

This task is about reconstructing general ledger accounts.

You are working on the accounting records of a sole trader for the year ended 31 May 20X2. The business is VAT registered.

You have the following information:

Daybook summaries	Goods £	VAT £	Total £
Sales	284,230	56,846	341,076
Sales returns	3,500	700	4,200

Further information:

Balances as at:	31 May 20X1 £	31 May 20X2 £
Trade receivables	50,050	39,600

- Cash sales of £6,600 were made, including VAT at 20%.
- The total banked was posted to the cash sales account.
- Prompt payment discounts were offered to credit customers.
- VAT has been correctly accounted for.

Receipts and payments recorded in the bank account	£
Amounts from credit customers	340,026

10

BPP
LEARNING MEDIA

Find the missing discounts allowed figure by preparing the sales ledger control account for the year ended 31 May 20X2.

Sales ledger control account

	£		£
▼		▼	
▼		▼	
▼		▼	
▼		▼	

Picklist:

Balance b/d
Balance c/d
Bank
Cash sales
Discounts allowed
Sales daybook
Sales returns daybook

Task 2.5

This task is about reconstructing general ledger accounts.

You are working on the accounting records of a sole trader for the year ended 31 August 20X6. The business is VAT registered.

You have the following information:

Daybook summaries	Goods £	VAT £	Total £
Purchases	162,000	32,400	194,400
Purchases returns	Not available		

Further information:

Balances as at:	31 August 20X5 £	31 August 20X6 £
Trade payables	31,450	42,320

- All purchases are on credit terms.
- The trader took advantage of prompt payment discounts whenever offered. Discounts received totalled £8,600 for the year.
- VAT has been correctly accounted for.

Receipts and payments recorded in the bank account	£
Amounts to suppliers	169,650

Find the missing purchases returns figure by preparing the purchases ledger control account for the year ended 31 August 20X6.

Purchases ledger control account

	£		£
▼		▼	
▼		▼	
▼		▼	
▼		▼	

Picklist:

Balance b/d
Balance c/d
Bank
Discounts received
Purchases daybook
Purchases returns daybook

Task 2.6

This task is about reconstructing general ledger accounts.

You are working on the accounting records of a sole trader for the year ended 31 October 20X7. The business is VAT registered.

You have the following information:

Daybook summaries	Goods £	VAT £	Total £
Sales	127,810	25,562	153,372
Sales returns	Not available		
Purchases	94,600	18,920	113,520
Purchases returns	2,840	568	3,408

Further information:

Balances as at:	31 October 20X6 £	31 October 20X7 £
VAT	6,560 credit	3,980 credit

- General expenses are not processed through the purchases daybook.

  £5,400 (including VAT at 20%) was posted to the general expenses account

  All the VAT on these expenses is recoverable.

- Cash sales of £8,600 were made, excluding VAT at 20%.

  The total banked was posted to the cash sales account.

- All purchases are on credit terms.

- The trader took advantage of prompt payment discounts whenever offered.

- VAT has been correctly accounted for.

Receipts and payments recorded in the bank account	£
HMRC for VAT – payment	9,230

Find the missing sales returns VAT figure by preparing the VAT ledger control account for the year ended 31 October 20X7.

VAT ledger control account

	£		£
▼		▼	
▼		▼	
▼		▼	
▼		▼	
▼		▼	

Picklist:

Balance b/d
Balance c/d
Bank
Cash sales
General expenses
Purchases daybook
Purchases returns daybook
Sales daybook
Sales returns daybook

....

Task 2.7

This task is about reconstructing general ledger accounts.

You are working on the accounting records of a sole trader for the year ended 30 November 20X8. The business is VAT registered.

You have the following information:

Nominal ledger balances as at:	30 November 20X7 £	30 November 20X8 £
Bank	8,400 credit	Not available

Further information:

Receipts and payments recorded in the bank account	£
Amounts from credit customers	100,500
Amounts to credit suppliers	68,340
Amounts banked from cash sales	9,400
Loan payment	4,380
Rent paid	24,000
General expenses	16,540
HMRC for VAT – receipt	3,790
Capital contribution from owner	18,000
Amounts refunded by credit suppliers	1,240

(a) **Find the closing bank balance (balance c/d) at 30 November 20X8 by preparing the bank ledger account.**

Bank ledger account

		£			£
	▼			▼	
	▼			▼	
	▼			▼	
	▼			▼	
	▼			▼	
	▼			▼	

Picklist:

Balance b/d
Balance c/d
Capital
Cash sales
General expenses
Loan
Purchases ledger control account
Rent
Sales ledger control account
VAT control account

(b) **Is the closing bank balance calculated in part (a) a positive cash balance or an overdraft?**

▼

Picklist:

Overdraft
Positive cash balance

Task 2.8

Information relating to the cash book for the year ended 31 January 20X8 is:

	£
Balance b/d at 1 February 20X7	9,870 credit
Balance c/d at 31 January 20X8	1,120 debit
Total receipts	156,000
Total payments	Not available

(a) **Assuming no adjustments are required, what are total payments for the year?**

£ [   ]

(b) **Will this entry be a debit or a credit in the bank account in the general ledger?**

▼

Picklist:

Debit
Credit

BPP
LEARNING MEDIA

Task 2.9

Where sales, purchases or inventory are unknown figures, mark-up or margin may be used to derive missing information.

Complete the following sentences:

[▼] is the profit as a percentage of sales.

[▼] is the profit as a percentage of cost.

Picklist:

Gross profit margin
Mark up

Task 2.10

Show how the following percentage is calculated.

Gross sales margin percentage [▼]

Picklist:

Current assets/current liabilities
Gross profit/sales × 100%
Inventory/Gross profit × 100%
Net profit/sales × 100%

Task 2.11

A shop operates with a mark-up on cost of 20%. Purchases for the month of May totalled £3,600. At the start of May inventory was £640 and at the end of May inventory was £570.

What were the sales for the month?

£ [   ]

Task 2.12

A shop operates with a mark-up on cost of 30%. Sales for the period were £5,200 and inventory at the start and end of the period were £300 and £500 respectively.

What are purchases for the period?

£ [ ]

Task 2.13

A shop operates on the basis of a profit margin of 20%. Purchases for the month of April totalled £5,010 and inventory at the start and the end of the month was £670 and £980 respectively.

What are the sales for the period?

£ [ ]

Task 2.14

A business has opening inventory of £30,000 and achieves a mark-up of 25% on cost. Sales totalled £1,000,000 and purchases were £840,000.

Calculate closing inventory.

	✓
£30,000	
£40,000	
£70,000	
£120,000	

Task 2.15

A business sells its goods at a mark-up on cost of 25%.

Standard rated VAT of 20% applies to all sales.

- The trader sells an item to a customer for £1,200 including VAT.
- There were no discounts.

Calculate the original cost of the item to the trader, excluding VAT.

£	

Task 2.16

A business sells its goods on the basis of a 30% profit margin.

Standard rated VAT of 20% applies to all sales.

- The trader sells an item to a customer for £1,800 including VAT.
- There were no discounts.

Calculate the original cost of the item to the trader, excluding VAT.

£	

Task 2.17

A sole trader has cost of goods sold of £280,000 during the year ended 30 June 20X7 and has invoices showing that his total purchases amounted to £279,800 in the same year.

The proprietor uses a standard pricing policy of a 20% gross profit margin and VAT is charged at 20%.

Using the information above, complete the following tasks:

(a) Calculate the sales to be included in the trial balance at 30 June 20X7.

£	

The year-end stock count showed that closing inventory was worth £29,000 at 30 June 20X7. This was £6,000 less than the balance at the beginning of the year.

(b) **Calculate the value of goods drawn by the owner in the current year.**

£ [   ]

The trader sells an item to a customer for £480, including VAT. There were no discounts and the rate of VAT is 20%.

(c) **Calculate the original cost to the trader.**

£ [   ]

The **trader** has not paid any more capital into the business during the current year. His net **assets** equalled £500,000 at 1 July 20X6 and his policy is to take a total of 25% of the gross profits of the company in drawings each year, comprising a mix of cash and inventory. The net profit for the year ending 30 June 20X7 was £38,000.

(d) **Calculate the closing balance on the capital account.**

£ [   ]

Task 2.18

You are an accounting technician working on the year end accounts for Sally, a sole trader making and distributing home-made goods at local markets. Sally's year end in 28 February 20X7.

You have noticed that inventory has increased by £150, compared to last year. The cost of goods sold amounts to £12,900 for the year ended 28 February 20X7. Sally is registered for VAT.

Using the information above, complete the following tasks:

(a) **Calculate the value of purchases, net of VAT for the year ended 28 February 20X7.**

£ [   ]

Inventory at the end of the year is unusually high due to a cancelled order. Sally usually likes to keep inventory equivalent to approximately half a month's average trading. That way, she avoids running out of stock but also avoids having her edible products expire.

(b) Complete the sentence by picking the most appropriate option from the picklist:

I would make an estimate of  for closing inventory.

Picklist:

£540
£1,000
£1,300
£600

The business sells goods at a mark-up on cost of 30%.

(c) Calculate the sales figure for inclusion in the trial balance at 28 February 20X7.

£ [   ]

In December, Sally sold a batch of aprons to a customer for £864 including VAT at 20%. There were no discounts.

(d) Calculate the original cost of the item to the trader, excluding VAT. Round your answer to the nearest £1.

£ [   ]

Chapter 3 – Accounts for sole traders

Task 3.1

Indicate with a tick whether each of the following balances are an asset, a liability, income, an expense or capital.

Account	Asset ✓	Liability ✓	Income ✓	Expense ✓	Capital ✓
Bank loan					
Bank overdraft					
Capital					
Office costs					
Prepayment					
Purchases					
Salaries					
Trade receivables					

Task 3.2

Given below is a trial balance for a business.

Show whether each item falls into the category of asset, liability, income, expense or capital.

Then show whether each item is included in the statement of profit or loss (SPL) or the statement of financial position (SOFP) in the final accounts.

Account	Debit £	Credit £	Asset, liability, income, expense or capital?	SPL or SOFP?
Advertising expenses	17,930		▼	▼
Bank	300		▼	▼
Capital		40,000	▼	▼
Computer equipment – cost	2,400		▼	▼
Discounts allowed	120		▼	▼
Discounts received		100	▼	▼
Distribution costs	400		▼	▼
Electricity expense	1,600		▼	▼
Motor vehicles – cost	32,600		▼	▼
Opening inventory	2,400		▼	▼
Purchases	97,100		▼	▼
Rent expense	11,400		▼	▼
Sales		153,900	▼	▼
Telephone costs	1,250		▼	▼
Trade receivables	11,900		▼	▼
Trade payables		6,000	▼	▼
Wages expense	20,600		▼	▼
	200,000	200,000		

Picklist:

Asset
Capital
Expense
Income
Liability
Statement of financial position (SOFP)
Statement of profit or loss (SPL)

Task 3.3

Fill in the missing words:

The trading account shows the [▼] profit for the period.

The final line of the statement of profit or loss shows the [▼].

Picklist:

gross
net assets
profit or loss for the period
total capital at the end of the period

Task 3.4

A business made sales during the year of £867,450. Purchases were £426,490.

Opening inventory was £24,580 and closing inventory was £30,570.

Distribution costs for the year were £104,370 and administration expenses totalled £87,690.

What is the gross profit and profit for the year?

Gross profit	£	
Profit for the year	£	

Task 3.5

Is the following statement correct?

	Yes ✓	No ✓
If a business has a bank overdraft, this is a current liability.		

Task 3.6

A sole trader had a capital balance of £32,570 on 1 May 20X4. During the year ended 30 April 20X5 the business made a profit for the year of £67,460.

The owner made drawings of £35,480 from the business bank account and withdraw goods costing £1,680 for personal use.

(a) **What is the capital balance at 30 April 20X5?**

£ _____

(b) **Complete the following:**

Drawings for the year will be a [　　　　　▼] to the capital account in the general ledger.

Picklist:

debit
credit

Task 3.7

A sole trader had a capital balance of £60,100 on 1 July 20X8. During the year ended 30 June 20X9 the business made a loss for the year of £24,500 and the owner made drawings of cash totalling £28,100 and goods with a cost of £900. The owner did not pay any additional capital into the business.

(a) **What is the capital balance at 30 June 20X9?**

£ _____

(b) Complete the following:

The loss for the year will be transferred as a [▼] to the capital account in the general ledger.

Picklist:

debit
credit

Task 3.8

On 1 January 20X8, a business had assets of £10,000 and liabilities of £7,000. By 31 December 20X8 it had assets of £15,000 and liabilities of £10,000. The owner paid £4,000 into the business bank account as a capital contribution. There were no drawings in the year.

Use the capital account below to calculate the profit or loss that arose in the year.

Capital account

	£		£
[▼]		[▼]	
[▼]		[▼]	

Picklist:

Balance b/d
Balance c/d
Bank
Loss
Profit

Task 3.9

The net assets of a business totalled £14,690 at 1 January 20X8 and £19,510 at 31 December 20X8. The owner did not pay any additional capital into the business. Drawings for the year were £9,670.

Use the capital account below to calculate the profit or loss made by the business in the year.

Capital account

	£			£
▼			▼	
▼			▼	

Picklist:

Balance b/d
Balance c/d
Drawings
Loss
Profit

....

Task 3.10

A business has net assets of £31,240 on 31 May 20X8. On 1 June 20X7 the net assets of the business were £26,450. The owner took £12,300 from the business bank account as drawings during the year and £560 of goods for his own use. The owner did not pay any capital into the business during the year.

Use the capital account below to calculate the profit or loss made by the business in the year.

Capital account

	£			£
▼			▼	
▼			▼	

Picklist:

Balance b/d
Balance c/d
Drawings
Loss
Profit

Task 3.11

A business had net assets at the start of the year of £23,700 and at the end of the year of £28,610. The business made a profit of £17,400 for the year. The owner did not pay any capital into the business during the year.

Use the capital account below to calculate the drawings made by the owner in the year.

Capital account

	£			£
▼			▼	
▼			▼	

Picklist:

Balance b/d
Balance c/d
Drawings
Loss
Profit

Task 3.12

A sole trader withdraw £1,200 from the business bank account for personal use.

What is the double entry to record this transaction?

Account name		Debit £	Credit £
	▼		
	▼		

Picklist:

Bank
Closing capital
Drawings
Opening capital
Profit
Purchases

Task 3.13

A sole trader took goods from his business with a cost of £800 for his own personal use.

What is the double entry to record this transaction?

Account name		Debit £	Credit £
	▼		
	▼		

Picklist:

Bank
Closing capital
Drawings
Opening capital
Profit
Purchases

Task 3.14

For a statement of financial position to balance, identify with a tick which ONE of the following statements is incorrect.

	✓
Net assets = owner's capital	
Net assets = capital + profit + drawings	
Net assets = capital + profit – drawings	
Assets – liabilities = capital + profit – drawings	

Task 3.15

A trial balance contains the following balances:

	£
Closing inventory	4,000
Opening inventory	2,000
Prompt payment discounts received	1,600
Purchases	20,000
Purchases returns	400

What is the cost of goods sold?

£	

Task 3.16

An extract to the trial balance of a sole trader includes the allowance for doubtful debts – adjustment as follows:

	Debit £	Credit £
Allowance for doubtful debts – adjustment	1,400	

Show where the allowance for doubtful debts – adjustment will be included in the statement of profit or loss. Leave any unused cells blank.

	£	£
Gross profit		X
Add:		
▼		
Less:		
▼		
Total expenses		X
Profit or loss for the year		X

Picklist:

Allowance for doubtful debts – adjustment

Task 3.17

An extract to the trial balance of a sole trader includes the allowance for doubtful debts – adjustment as follows:

	Debit £	Credit £
Allowance for doubtful debts – adjustment		800

Show where the allowance for doubtful debts – adjustment will be included in the statement of profit or loss. Leave any unused cells blank.

	£	£
Gross profit		X
Add:		
▼		
Less:		
▼		
Total expenses		X
Profit or loss for the year		X

Picklist:

Allowance for doubtful debts – adjustment

Task 3.18

An extract to the trial balance of a sole trader includes the following balances:

	Debit £	Credit £
Closing inventory	11,000	11,000
Discounts allowed	1,680	
Discounts received		880
Miscellaneous expenses	32,220	
Opening inventory	12,500	
Purchases	46,400	
Sales		83,400

Complete the statement of profit or loss extract using the balances listed above.

If necessary, use a minus sign to indicate ONLY the following:

- **The deduction of an account balance used to make up cost of goods sold**

- **A loss for the year**

	£	£
Sales revenue		
▼		
▼		
▼		
▼		
Cost of goods sold		
Gross profit		
Add:		
▼		

		£	£
Less:			
	▼		
	▼		
	▼		
Total expenses			
Profit or loss for the year			

Picklist:

Closing inventory
Discounts allowed
Discounts received
Miscellaneous expenses
Opening inventory
Purchases
Sales revenue

Task 3.19

An extract to the trial balance of a sole trader includes the following details for non-current assets:

	Debit £	Credit £
Equipment at cost	60,000	
Equipment accumulated depreciation		12,000

Record the non-current asset in the statement of financial position extract. Do NOT use brackets, minus signs or dashes.

	Cost £	Accumulated depreciation £	Carrying amount £
Non-current assets			
▼			

Picklist:

Bank
Depreciation charges
Equipment

....

Task 3.20

[This preparation task is longer than an AAT assessment-style task.]

This task is about final accounts for sole traders. You are preparing the statement of profit or loss and statement of financial position for Helm Trading as at 30 April 20X4.

The final trial balance as at 30 April 20X4 is below.

Trial balance at 30 April 20X4

	Debit £	Credit £
Accruals		1,000
Allowance for doubtful debts		1,200
Allowance for doubtful debts – adjustment		2,000
Bank		1,650
Capital		74,000
Closing inventory	43,500	43,500
Depreciation charges	10,250	
Discounts allowed	2,950	
Drawings	30,000	
Furniture and fittings at cost	72,500	
Furniture and fittings accumulated depreciation		38,350
Irrecoverable debts	1,700	
Miscellaneous expenses	1,500	
Opening inventory	41,000	
Prepayments	1,500	
Purchases	245,000	

BPP
LEARNING MEDIA

	Debit £	Credit £
Purchases ledger control account		40,800
Rent	13,700	
Sales		369,000
Sales ledger control account	60,000	
VAT		4,100
Wages	52,000	
	575,600	575,600

(a) **You are to prepare the statement of profit or loss for Helm Trading as at 30 April 20X4.**

If necessary, use a minus sign to indicate ONLY the following:

- **The deduction of an account balance used to make up cost of goods sold**

- **A loss for the year**

Helm Trading

Statement of profit or loss for the year ended 30 April 20X4

		£	£
Sales revenue			
	▼		
	▼		
	▼		
	▼		
Cost of goods sold			
Gross profit			
Add:			
	▼		

	£	£
Less:		
▼		
▼		
▼		
▼		
▼		
▼		
Total expenses		
Profit or loss for the year		

Picklist:

Accruals
Allowance for doubtful debts
Allowance for doubtful debts – adjustment
Bank
Bank overdraft
Capital
Closing inventory
Depreciation charges
Discounts allowed
Drawings
Furniture and fittings at cost
Furniture and fittings accumulated depreciation
Irrecoverable debts
Miscellaneous expenses
Opening inventory
Prepayments
Purchases
Purchases ledger control account
Rent
Sales
Sales ledger control account
VAT
Wages

(b) **You are to prepare the statement of financial position for Helm Trading as at 30 April 20X4. Do NOT use brackets, minus signs or dashes.**

- The profit or loss from the year calculated in part (a) must be included in the statement of financial position.

- Helm Trading has a policy of showing trade receivables net of any allowance for doubtful debts.

Helm Trading

Statement of financial position as at 30 April 20X4

	Cost £	Accumulated depreciation £	Carrying amount £
Non-current assets			
(1) ▼			
Current assets			
(1) ▼			
(1) ▼			
(1) ▼			
(1) ▼			
Current liabilities			
(1) ▼			
(1) ▼			
(1) ▼			
(1) ▼			
(1) ▼			
Net current assets			
Net assets			

Financed by:			
Capital			
Opening capital			
(2) ▼			
(2) ▼			
Closing capital			

Picklist (1):

Accruals
Allowance for doubtful debts
Allowance for doubtful debts – adjustment
Bank
Bank overdraft
Capital
Depreciation charges
Discounts allowed
Furniture and fittings
Inventory
Irrecoverable debts expense
Miscellaneous expenses
Prepayments
Purchases
Rent
Sales
Trade payables
Trade receivables
VAT
Wages

Picklist (2):

Add: Drawings
Add: Profit for the year
Less: Drawings
Less: Profit for the year

Chapter 4 – Accounts for partnerships

Task 4.1

Fill in the missing word regarding the definition of a partnership.

A partnership is a relationship between persons carrying on a business in common with a view to:

| | ▼ | . |

Picklist:

creating a separate legal entity
profit

Task 4.2

What is the double entry for drawings made by a partner from the business bank account?

Debit		▼
Credit		▼

Picklist:

Bank
Loan
Partner's capital account
Partner's current account
Purchases

Task 4.3

What is the double entry to record interest earned on a partner's capital account balance?

Debit		▼
Credit		▼

Task 4.4

This task is about accounting for partnerships. The partners are Jim, Rob and Fiona.

Figures relating to the year ended 31 December 20X8 were as follows:

	Jim	Rob	Fiona
Profit share	40%	40%	20%
	£	£	£
Current account balances on 1 January 20X8	8,000 credit	1,000 debit	6,500 credit
Drawings for the year	58,000	40,000	32,000

Profit for the year ended 31 December 20X8 was £135,000 before appropriations. Under the partnership agreement, the profit share is the only appropriation.

Prepare the partners' current accounts for the year ended 31 December 20X8. Show the balance b/d on 1 January 20X9.

Current account – Jim

	£		£
▼		▼	
▼		▼	
▼		▼	
▼		▼	

Current account – Rob

	£		£
▼		▼	
▼		▼	
▼		▼	
▼		▼	

Current account – Fiona

	£		£
▼		▼	
▼		▼	
▼		▼	
▼		▼	

Picklist:

Balance b/d
Balance c/d
Drawings
Share of profit or loss

Task 4.5

This task is about accounting for partnerships. The year end is 31 May.

Ian and Max have been in partnership for many years. On 31 May 20X8, Len is to be admitted into the partnership. Len is to make a capital contribution into the business bank account of £32,600.

Profit share, effective before the admission of Len:

Ian   60%
Max   40%

Profit share, effective after the admission of Len:

Ian	40%
Max	40%
Len	20%

Goodwill was valued at £18,000 and has not yet been entered in the accounting records.

Goodwill is to be introduced into the accounting records on 31 May 20X8 with the partnership change and then immediately eliminated.

Prepare the partners' capital accounts for the year ended 31 May 20X8, showing clearly the individual entries for the introduction and elimination of goodwill and the balance c/d.

Capital accounts

	Ian £	Max £	Len £		Ian £	Max £	Len £
▼				Balance b/d	85,000	60,000	
▼				▼			
▼				▼			

Picklist:

Balance b/d
Balance c/d
Bank
Goodwill
Share of profit or loss

Task 4.6

Theo, Deb and Fran have been in partnership for a number of years. However, on 31 December 20X8 Deb is to retire.

The credit balances on the partners' capital and current accounts at that date are:

	Theo £	Deb £	Fran £
Capital	84,000	62,000	37,000
Current	4,500	1,300	6,200

Profit share, effective before the retirement of Deb:

Theo   60%
Deb   30%
Fran   10%

Profit share, effective after the retirement of Deb:

Theo   75%
Fran   25%

The goodwill of the partnership on 31 December 20X8 is estimated to be £54,000.

The agreement with Deb is that £10,000 from her capital account will be repaid at the date of retirement and the remainder of the amount that is due to her will take the form of a loan to the partnership.

(a)   **Using the information above, prepare the partners' capital and current accounts to reflect Deb's retirement. Show the balance c/d at the end of the period.**

Capital accounts

	Theo £	Deb £	Fran £		Theo £	Deb £	Fran £
▼				▼			
▼				▼			
▼				▼			
▼				▼			

Current accounts

	Theo £	Deb £	Fran £		Theo £	Deb £	Fran £
▼				▼			
▼				▼			

Picklist:

Balance b/d
Balance c/d
Bank
Capital accounts
Current accounts
Goodwill
Loan
Share of profit or loss

(b) **Complete the following sentence by selecting the appropriate phrase from the picklist in each case:**

When a partner retires from a partnership business, the balance on the [▼] must be transferred to the [▼] .

Picklist:

partner's capital account
partner's current account

Task 4.7

Josh and Ken have been the owners of a partnership business for many years.

An extract from their trial balance at 30 June 20X8 is given below.

	Josh	Ken
Profit share	70%	30%
	£	£
Salary entitlement per month	0	500
Sales commission earned during the year	800	2,500
Interest on capital earned during the year	400	250
Drawings	20,000	17,400
Current account balances (before adjustment at 30 June 20X8)	1,300 credit	800 credit

Profit for the year ended 30 June 20X8 was £39,950 before appropriations.

(a) **Prepare the appropriation accounts for the partnerships for the year ended 30 June 20X8.**

You MUST enter zeros where appropriate in order to obtain full marks.

Use a minus sign for deductions or where there is a loss to be distributed.

Partnership appropriation account for the year ended 30 June 20X8

	£	
Profit for appropriation		
▼		Enter any deductions as negative eg –999
▼		
▼		
▼		
▼		
▼		
Residual profit available for distribution		

Share of residual profit or loss:	
▼	
▼	
Total residual profit or loss distributed	

Picklist:

Drawings – Josh
Drawings – Ken
Interest on capital – Josh
Interest on capital – Ken
Salary – Josh
Salary – Ken
Sales commission – Josh
Sales commission – Ken
Share of profit or loss – Josh
Share of profit or loss – Ken

(b) **Using the information above, prepare the partners' current accounts. Show the balance c/d and balance b/d at the end of the period.**

Current account – Josh

	£		£
▼		▼	
▼		▼	
▼		▼	
▼		▼	
▼		▼	

Picklist:

Balance b/d
Balance c/d
Drawings
Interest on capital
Salary
Sales commission
Share of profit or loss

Current account – Ken

	£			£
▼		▼		
▼		▼		
▼		▼		
▼		▼		
▼		▼		
▼		▼		

Picklist:

Balance b/d
Balance c/d
Drawings
Interest on capital
Salary
Sales commission
Share of profit or loss

Task 4.8

Derek and Eva have been in partnership for a number of years.

- Fabio was admitted to the partnership on 1 April 20X1 when he introduced £60,000 to the bank account.

- Profit share, effective until 31 March 20X1:

  - Derek 50%
  - Eva 50%

- Profit share, effective from 1 April 20X1:

  - Derek 40%
  - Eva 40%
  - Fabio 20%

- Goodwill was valued at £44,000 on 31 March 20X1.

- Goodwill is to be introduced into the partners' capital accounts on 31 March and then eliminated on 1 April.

Prepare the capital account for Fabio, the new partner, showing clearly the balance carried down as at 1 April 20X1.

Capital account – Fabio

	£			£
▼		▼		
▼		▼		

Picklist:

Balance b/d
Balance c/d
Bank
Goodwill

Task 4.9

This task is about final accounts for partnerships.

You are preparing the statement of profit or loss for the Madison partnership for the year ended 31 July 20X4.

The partners are Jo and Emily, who share profits and losses equally. This is their only entitlement to profit.

You have the final trial balance below. All the necessary year-end adjustments have been made, except for the transfer of profit or loss and drawings to the current accounts of the partners.

(a) **Prepare the statement of profit or loss for the Madison Partnership for the year ended 31 July 20X4.**

If necessary, use a minus sign to indicate ONLY the following:

- **The deduction of an account balance used to make up cost of goods sold**

- **A loss for the year**

Madison Partnership

Trial balance as at 31 July 20X4

	Debit £	Credit £
Accruals		400
Advertising	4,940	
Allowance for doubtful debts		1,500
Allowance for doubtful debts – adjustment	1,500	
Bank	5,820	
Bank interest		50
Capital – Jo		30,000
Capital – Emily		20,000
Closing inventory	9,000	9,000
Current – Jo		1,000
Current – Emily		600
Depreciation charges	11,080	
Drawings – Jo	12,000	
Drawings – Emily	20,000	
Furniture at cost	50,500	
Furniture accumulated depreciation		15,400
Office expenses	2,400	
Opening inventory	13,300	
Payroll expenses	5,100	
Prepayments	950	
Purchases	186,410	
Purchases ledger control account		33,100
Sales		265,550

	Debit £	Credit £
Sales ledger control account	55,000	
VAT		1,400
Total	**378,000**	**378,000**

Maddison Partnership

Statement of profit or loss for the year ended 31 July 20X4

		£	£
Sales revenue			

	▼		
	▼		
	▼		
Cost of goods sold			
Gross profit			
Add:			
	▼		
Less:			
	▼		
	▼		
	▼		
	▼		
	▼		
	▼		
Total expenses			
Profit/loss for the year			

Picklist:

Accruals
Advertising
Allowance for doubtful debts
Allowance for doubtful debts – adjustment
Bank
Bank interest
Capital accounts
Closing inventory
Current accounts
Depreciation charges
Drawings – Jo
Drawings – Emily
Furniture
Office expenses
Opening inventory
Payroll expenses
Prepayments
Purchases
Purchases ledger control account
Sales
Sales ledger control account
VAT

(b) **Calculate Jo and Emily's share the profit or loss for the year.**

Use a minus sign to indicate ONLY a loss for the year, if necessary.

	£
Jo – share of profit or loss	
Emily – share of profit or loss	

(c) **Calculate Jo and Emily's final current account balance at the end of the year.**

	£
Jo – final current account balance	
Emily – final current account balance	

(d) **Prepare the statement of financial position of the Madison Partnership as at 31 July 20X4.**

Maddison Partnership

Statement of financial position as at 31 July 20X4

	Cost £	Accumulated depreciation £	Carrying amount £
Non-current assets			
▼			
Current assets			
▼			
▼			
▼			
▼			
▼			
Current liabilities			
▼			
▼			
▼			
▼			
▼			
Net current assets			
Net assets			

Financed by:		Jo	Emily	Total
	▼			
	▼			

Picklist:

Accruals
Advertising
Allowance for doubtful debts
Allowance for doubtful debts – adjustment
Bank
Bank interest
Capital accounts
Closing inventory
Current accounts
Depreciation charges
Drawings – Jo
Drawings – Emily
Furniture
Inventory
Office expenses
Opening inventory
Payroll expenses
Prepayments
Purchases
Sales
Trade payables
Trade receivables
VAT

Chapter 5 – Introduction to limited company accounts

Task 5.1

Identify the most likely reason as to why different user groups are interested in the final accounts.

Reason for their interest in the final accounts	User groups
View the accounts with the objective of assessing the tax payable by the organisation	▼
View the accounts with the objective of understanding the organisation's ability to pay its debts	▼
View the accounts as the organisation affects them in many ways (eg by providing jobs and using local suppliers, or by affecting the environment)	▼
View the accounts with a view to assessing the current daily activities of the company, to assist with planning decisions	▼

Picklist:

Credit suppliers
Management
Tax authorities
The public

Task 5.2

Limited companies are required to obey Accounting standards and Company Law.

Why is it important that all companies follow the same accounting standards when they are accounting for financial transactions and producing financial statements?

Select the most important option.

	✓
So that accurate information is submitted to the taxation authority	
So that users are able to understand the financial statements and compare them year on year and from one company to another	
So that investors can see the difference in working capital between a manufacturing company and a service provider	
To remove any differences between companies that are funded through loan capital as opposed to those that are funded through a public listing	

Task 5.3

Which body is responsible for setting International Financial Reporting Standards? Select ONE option.

	✓
Companies Act 2006	
Charities Act 2011	
International Accounting Standard 1 (IAS 1)	
International Accounting Standards Board	

Task 5.4

For a company that has adopted International Financial Reporting Standards, which source prescribes the required format for the statement of profit or loss and statement of financial position?

Select ONE option.

	✓
Companies Act 2006	
Charities Act 2011	
International Accounting Standard 1 (IAS 1)	
International Accounting Standards Board	

Task 5.5

The provisions of the Companies Act 2006 applies to which of the following UK-based organisations? Select TWO options.

	✓
Sole traders	
Partnership (unincorporated)	
Limited liability partnership	
Limited company	

Task 5.6

Why is it important for companies to ensure that the directors and employees have up-to-date knowledge of relevant legislation and accounting standards? Select TWO options.

	✓
To ensure compliance with the Companies Act 2006.	
To maximise shareholder wealth.	
To enable the company to pay tax as it falls due to the tax authorities.	
To demonstrate a strong statement of financial position.	
To ensure compliance with International Financial Reporting Standards.	

Task 5.7

Complete the following sentence:

Financial statements for limited companies must be prepared at least [_____▼] and filed at Companies House.

Picklist

annually
every six months
once every two years

Task 5.8

Show whether the following statements are true or false:

		Answer
The Companies Act states that notes must be provided as part of the financial statements of a company.		▼
The Companies Act states that notes must be provided as part of the accounts for a sole trader.		▼

Picklist:

True
False

Task 5.9

Who are the primary users of the final accounts of companies?

Primary users	
	▼
	▼

Picklist:

Credit customers
Employees
Existing and potential investors
Lenders and other creditors
The public

Task 5.10

The framework also recognises that a variety of different groups have a need for financial statements.

Complete the sentence below:

An employee may require information from a set of limited company accounts to

	▼

Picklist:

assess the company's ability to repay the capital amount of the long-term loan
assess the company's ability to pay out pensions in the future
assess the company's ability to pay dividends in the coming year

Task 5.11

Which of the following standards provides guidance for property, plant and equipment, where IFRS is adopted? Select ONE option.

	✓
IAS 1	
IAS 2	
IAS 6	
IAS 16	

Task 5.12

Which of the following standards provides guidance for inventories, where IFRS is adopted? Select ONE option.

	✓
IAS 1	
IAS 2	
IAS 6	
IAS 16	

Task 5.13

Which of the following is not a qualitative characteristic, under the *Conceptual Framework*? Select ONE option.

	✓
Comparability	
Going concern	
Faithful representation	
Relevance	

Task 5.14

Select the underlying assumption governing accounts which matches the following descriptions.

Description	Underlying Assumption
The effect of transactions and other events are recognised when they occur and are reported in the period to which they relate.	▼
The financial statements are normally prepared on the assumption that an entity will continue in operation for the foreseeable future.	▼

Picklist:

Accruals
Consistency
Going concern
Materiality

Task 5.15

A business is being forced to cease operating. The assets of the business must be recognised at the amount expected to arise from their sale and liabilities must be recognised at the amounts that they are likely to be settled at.

Which assumption is being applied here?

▼

Picklist:

Accruals
Comparability
Going concern
Materiality

Task 5.16

The conceptual framework that forms the basis for all financial reporting standards splits the qualitative characteristics of financial statements into fundamental qualitative characteristics and enhancing characteristics.

Drag and drop the correct words into the boxes below to complete the sentences:

The *Conceptual Framework* identifies two fundamental qualitative characteristics of useful financial information. They are [   ] and [   ] .

Picklist:

relevance	timeliness	understandability
verifiability	going concern	materiality
accruals	comparability	faithful representation

Task 5.17

Which of the following characteristics enable financial information to faithfully represent the phenomenon it purports to represent? Select THREE options.

Characteristics	✓
Neutral	
Confirmatory value	
Clear, concise information	
Free from error	
Complete	
Available to decision makers in time to be capable of influencing their decisions	

Task 5.18

Which of the following characteristics enable financial information to be relevant in making a difference in the decisions made by users? Select TWO options.

Characteristics	✓
Assures users that information faithfully represents the economic phenomenon it purports to represent	
Confirmatory value	
Classifying, characterising and presenting information clearly and concisely.	
Free from error	
Predictive value	
Available to decision makers in time to be capable of influencing their decisions	

Task 5.19

One of the enhancing qualitative characteristics is that 'information is more useful if it can be compared with similar information about other entities and other periods.'

Which qualitative characteristic is described here?

Picklist:

Comparability
Timeliness
Understandability
Verifiability

Task 5.20

For the year ended 31 December 20X7, a company has reported a profit of £100,000 in its draft accounts. While the accounts are being finalised, it is found that due to an error, this profit has been overstated by £25,000.

On the basis of the draft profit, the bank has provisionally agreed to make a loan to the company. However, if this error is corrected, the bank will be unlikely to go ahead with the loan.

Which accounting concept is relevant here?

Picklist:

Going concern
Materiality
Timeliness
Understandability

Task 5.21

Answer the questions below regarding the different types of organisation:

(a)   State whether the following statements are true or false:

	True	False
Expenses for a partnership are classified into three separate groups, namely cost of goods sold, admin expenses and distribution expenses.		
The taxation expense must be separately disclosed on the face of a company's statement of profit or loss.		
The equity interest in a limited company is presented as share capital on the face of the statement of financial position.		

(b)   Which ONE of the following statements best describes a benefit of running a business as a company rather than a partnership?

	✓
There is more than one owner in a company so responsibility for running the business will be split.	
Running a company is less costly than running a partnership due to the is tighter regulation and standards that a company must obey.	
A sole trader does not need to produce year-end financial statements.	
A public company can easily raise additional capital finance on the open market, through selling shares.	

(c) **Which ONE of the following statements regarding limited liability is true?**

	✓
The non-current liabilities of a company are limited to a certain amount.	
The shareholders of a company have joint and severable liability in the case of liquidation.	
In the case of liquidation, the shareholder's liability is limited to the value of their investment.	
The partners in a limited liability partnership have unlimited liability in the case of liquidation.	

Answer Bank

Chapter 1

Task 1.1

Description	Type of organisation
A business that is a separate legal entity from its owners; the owners have shares in the business.	Limited company
An organisation that meets the definition of a charity as set out in the Charities Act 2011. It is established for charitable purposes only.	Charity
An unincorporated business owned and managed by two or more people.	Partnership (unincorporated)
An unincorporated business owned and managed by one person.	Sole trader
A business that is a separate legal entity owned and managed by two or more people.	Limited liability partnership

Task 1.2

Sole traders and partnerships are | unincorporated businesses |. This means there is | no legal distinction | between the business and their owners. Consequently, sole traders and partners have | unlimited liability | for the business's obligations.

Task 1.3

Options	✓
In the event that the business generates a loss, this is shared by the partners instead of being borne by a sole trader only.	
Any debts of the business are which cannot be met from the business assets are met from the owners' private resources.	
In the event that the business generates a profit, this is due to the sole trader only.	✓
The sole trader is not liable for the debts of the business.	

Explanation:

Statement 1 – This describes a benefit of working in a partnership; any loss that arises in a sole trader's organisation will be borne by the owner alone.

Statement 2 – This is a disadvantage of operating as a sole trader rather than an advantage.

Statement 3 – This is a key benefit of operating as a sole trader.

Statement 4 – This is incorrect as sole traders are liable for the debts of the business.

Task 1.4

Options	✓
The company's shareholders are not personally liable for the debts of the business.	✓
The company directors must ensure the accounts are filed at Companies House by a specified date.	
Companies must comply with the provisions of the Companies Act whereas unincorporated businesses do not.	
The company's tax charge must be shown in the statement of profit or loss.	

Explanation:

Statements 2 to 4 are consequences of incorporation rather than benefits.

Statement 3 is a disadvantage of incorporation rather than an advantage.

Task 1.5

Statement	Answer
When a sole trader takes money from the business for personal use, this is known as	drawings
In addition to a salary, a director (who is also a shareholder) of a limited liability company may be paid a	dividend

Task 1.6

Type of organisation	✓
Sole trader	
Partnership (unincorporated)	
Limited liability partnership	
Limited company	✓
Charity	

Explanation:

As limited companies are separate legal entities, they are taxed in their own right. Therefore, tax will appear in the financial statements of limited companies.

However, tax does not appear in the accounts of unincorporated businesses as the owners are taxed personally on the profits of the business. Likewise, limited liability partnership (LLP) members are self-employed for tax purposes and therefore the LLP itself is not taxed as a whole.

Registered charities do not pay tax on most types of income.

Task 1.7

Description of the organisation's tax position	Type of organisation(s)
Organisations that meet the definition of a charity and that are registered with the Charities Commission do not pay tax on most types of income.	Charity
Tax will not be classed as a business expense in the statement of profit or loss; each partner must prepare a self-assessment tax return.	Limited liability partnership and Partnership (unincorporated)
Tax will not be classed as a business expense in the statement of profit or loss; the owner of the business must prepare a self-assessment tax return.	Sole trader

Task 1.8

Action	✓
Obey the owner as it is his company.	
Explain that accounting policies have to reflect the most appropriate accounting treatment and that they cannot be changed simply to improve reported profit.	✓
Report the owner to the police.	

Explanation:

Accounting policies must be selected on the basis that they will enable the final accounts to give a fair view of the organisation's results for the period and its assets and liabilities at the end of the period. Therefore, statement 2 is correct.

Statement 1 – You have been engaged to prepare the final accounts and therefore have a duty to ensure they are prepared accurately and in accordance with the applicable regulations. Also, you have a duty to adhere to the *AAT Code of Professional Ethics* for accountants. In this particular case, you could not obey the owner simply because it is his company.

Statement 3 – This is not appropriate in this situation as it is too extreme a response especially when no illegal act appears to have been committed. The appropriate action is to apply the most reasonable depreciation charge when the accounts are prepared.

Task 1.9

Action	✓
Agree that this is a sensible course of action.	
Explain that the information provided by your client is confidential and that you cannot risk sensitive information being seen by a member of the public.	✓

Explanation:

Accountants have a duty not to share confidential information with third parties without specific permission from the business. Therefore, preparing the final accounts in a public area is not appropriate.

Task 1.10

Action	✓
Email the client explaining that your firm must decline the engagement.	
Attempt to prepare the accounts yourself, including the inventories figure.	
Speak to your manager and request support in this assignment.	✓

Explanation:

Statement 1 – There will be sufficient knowledge within your firm and therefore you do not need to decline the engagement.

Statement 2 – You should not attempt to prepare the accounts yourself as you do not have adequate knowledge to do this.

Statement 3 – As you do not have sufficient technical knowledge to prepare the final accounts yourself, you must request support.

Task 1.11

Risks	✓
Objectivity is a risk here. Your uncle owns Sandbury Trading. If you prepare the accounts for this organisation, it could be perceived that you may be biased towards presenting financial information in your uncle's favour.	✓
Confidentiality is a risk as you will need Sandbury Trading's financial information in order to prepare the final accounts.	
Professional competence and due care is a risk as it seems that you are not qualified to prepare the final accounts.	

Explanation:

If you prepare the final accounts for your uncle, objectivity is the main principle at risk. Self-interest and familiarity threats are relevant here.

Due to this family relationship, it could be perceived that you may present financial information so that it is favourable for your uncle. For example, if assets are overstated, this may help your uncle obtain finance.

Chapter 2

Task 2.1

Options	✓
It appears in the statement of profit or loss only.	
There was an issue with the IT system and backups had not been kept.	✓
An employee failed to record certain transactions.	✓
An error was made when posting the depreciation charge for the year.	

Task 2.2

Options	✓
The totals of the sales day book were overstated.	
Payments made to credit suppliers were omitted from the suppliers' accounts in the purchases ledger.	
Invoices sent to credit customers were duplicated in the sales ledger.	✓
Bank receipts from credit customers were duplicated in the sales ledger.	

Explanation:

Statement 1 – If the totals of the sales day book are overstated, the balance on the sales ledger control account will be higher than the total of the sales ledger balances. Therefore, option 1 is incorrect.

Statement 2 – This affects the purchases ledger only; it does not affect the sales ledger and sales ledger control account.

Statement 3 – Duplicating sales invoices in the sales ledger will result in the total sales ledger balances being higher than the balance on the sales ledger control account.

Statement 4 – If bank receipts were duplicated in the sales ledger, the total of the sales ledger balances will be lower than the balance on the sales ledger control account.

Task 2.3

Options	✓
Invoices sent to customers in respect of credit sales	
Invoice received from suppliers in respect of credit purchases	
Capital contributions from the owner into the business bank account	
Sundry expenses paid from petty cash	✓

Explanation:

Statements 1 and 2 – Transactions with credit customers and credit suppliers require invoices. Therefore, financial information will be readily available.

Statement 3 – A capital contribution paid into the business bank account will be seen on the bank statement and therefore financial information is available on this transaction.

Statement 4 – Where cash payments are made, and in particular small amounts are withdrawn from the petty cash tin, it is possible that employees will forget to obtain cash receipts to support purchases. Therefore, financial documentation providing evidence of sundry purchases may not be readily available.

However, it is important that organisations have strong policies which encourage employees to obtain evidence of all transactions.

Task 2.4

Sales ledger control account

	£		£
Balance b/d	50,050	Sales returns daybook	4,200
Sales daybook	341,076	Bank	340,026
		Discounts allowed	**7,300**
		Balance c/d	39,600
	391,126		391,126

Explanation:

Only transactions relating to credit customers are recorded in the sales ledger control account. Therefore, cash sales are excluded. Discounts allowed is calculated as the balancing figure.

Task 2.5

Purchases ledger control account

	£		£
Bank	169,650	Balance b/d	31,450
Discounts received	8,600	Purchases daybook	194,400
Purchases returns daybook	**5,280**		
Balance c/d	42,320		
	225,850		225,850

Task 2.6

VAT ledger control account

	£		£
Purchases daybook	18,920	Balance b/d	6,560
General expenses (5,400 × 20/120)	900	Sales daybook	25,562
Bank	9,230	Cash sales (8,600 × 20%)	1,720
Sales returns daybook	**1,380**	Purchases returns daybook	568
Balance c/d	3,980		
	34,410		34,410

Task 2.7

(a) Bank ledger account

	£		£
Sales ledger control account	100,500	Balance b/d	8,400
Cash sales	9,400	Purchases ledger control account	68,340
Purchases ledger control account	1,240	Loan	4,380
VAT control account	3,790	Rent	24,000
Capital	18,000	General expenses	16,540
		Balance c/d	**11,270**
	132,930		132,930

(b)

Positive cash balance

Explanation:

The closing balance is a balance c/d the right hand side of the T-account at the end of the period. To complete the double entry, at the start of the next period the balance is brought down on the opposite side of the T-account. As it will be brought down on the left side which is the debit side at the start of the next period, it is an asset and therefore the business has a positive bank balance.

Task 2.8

(a)

£	147,250

Workings

Bank

	£		£
Total receipts	156,000	Balance b/d	9,870
Balance c/d	1,120	**Total payments**	**147,250**
	157,120		157,120

(b)

Credit

Explanation:

Payments from the bank account in the general ledger reduce the bank asset. Therefore, they are entered on the credit side of the bank account in the general ledger.

Task 2.9

| Gross profit margin | is the profit as a percentage of sales.

| Mark up | is the profit as a percentage of cost.

Task 2.10

Gross sales margin percentage | Gross profit/sales × 100% |

Task 2.11

£	4,404

Workings

	%	£
Sales (3,670 × 120/100)	120	4,404
Cost of goods sold (640 + 3,600 – 570)	100	3,670
Gross profit	20	734

Task 2.12

£	4,200

Workings

	%	£	£
Sales	130		5,200
Cost of goods sold			
Opening inventory		300	
Purchases (balancing figure)		4,200	
		4,500	
Less: closing inventory		(500)	
Cost of goods sold (5,200 × 100/130)	100		4,000
Gross profit	30		1,200

Task 2.13

£	5,875

Workings

	%	£
Sales (4,700 × 100/80)	100	5,875
Cost of goods sold (670 + 5,010 – 980)	80	4,700
Gross profit	20	1,175

Task 2.14

	✓
£30,000	
£40,000	
£70,000	✓
£120,000	

Workings

	%	£	£
Sales	125		1,000,000
Cost of goods sold			
Opening inventory		30,000	
Purchases		840,000	
		870,000	
Less: closing inventory (balancing figure)		(70,000)	
Cost of goods sold (1,000,000 × 100/125)	100		800,000
Gross profit	25		200,000

Task 2.15

£	800

Workings

1   VAT: £1,200 × 20/120 = £200

2   Net: £1,200 − £200 = £1,000

3

	%	£
Sales (W2)	125	1,000
Cost of goods sold (1,000 × 100/125)	100	800
Gross profit	25	200

Task 2.16

£	1,050

Workings

1   VAT: £1,800 × 20/120 = £300

2   Net: £1,800 − £300 = £1,500

3

	%	£
Sales (W2)	100	1,500
Cost of goods sold (1,500 × 70/100)	70	1,050
Gross profit	30	450

Task 2.17

(a)

£	350,000

Workings

	%	£
Sales (280,000 × 100/80)	100	**350,000**
Cost of goods sold	80	280,000
Gross profit (350,000 – 280,000)	20	70,000

(b)

£	5,800

Workings

	£	£
Cost of goods sold		
Opening inventory (29,000 + 6,000)		35,000
Purchases	279,800	
Less: drawings (280,000 + 29,000 – 35000 – 279,800)	**(5,800)**	
		274,000
		309,000
Closing Inventory		(29,000)
Cost of goods sold		280,000

(c)

£	320

Workings

	%	£
Sales (480 × 100/120)	100	400
Cost of goods sold (400 × 80/100)	80	**320**
Gross profit	20	80

(d)

£	520,500

Workings

	£
Capital at 1 July 20X6	500,000
Profit	38,000
Less: drawings (70,000 × 25%)	(17,500)
Capital at 30 June 20X7	**520,500**

Task 2.18

(a)

£	13,050

Workings

	£
Inventory at 1 March 20X6	0
Purchases (12,900 + 150)	**13,050**
Less: Inventory at 28 February 20X7	(150)
Cost of goods sold	12,900

(b)

£	540

Working: Cost of goods sold for the year represents the average cost of trading for the year. The inventory holding is equivalent to half a month's trading, which is £12,900 (cost of goods sold)/24 (half a month) = £537.50, which rounds off to £540 as the nearest £10.

(c)

£	16,770

Workings

	%	£
Sales (12,900 × 130/100)	130	**16,770**
Cost of goods sold	100	12,900
Gross profit	30	3,870

(d)

£	554

Workings

	%	£
Sales (864 × 100/120)	130	720
Cost of goods sold (W2: 720 × 100/130)	100	**554**
Gross profit	30	166

Chapter 3

Task 3.1

Account	Asset ✓	Liability ✓	Income ✓	Expense ✓	Capital ✓
Bank loan		✓			
Bank overdraft		✓			
Capital					✓
Office costs				✓	
Prepayment	✓				
Purchases				✓	
Salaries				✓	
Trade receivables	✓				

Task 3.2

Account	Debit £	Credit £	Asset, liability, income, expense or capital?	SPL or SOFP?
Advertising expenses	17,930		Expense	SPL
Bank	300		Asset	SOFP
Capital		40,000	Capital	SOFP
Computer equipment – cost	2,400		Asset	SOFP
Discounts allowed	120		Expense	SPL
Discounts received		100	Income	SPL
Distribution costs	400		Expense	SPL
Electricity expense	1,600		Expense	SPL

Account	Debit	Credit	Asset, liability, income, expense or capital?	SPL or SOFP?
	£	£		
Motor vehicles – cost	32,600		Asset	SOFP
Opening inventory	2,400		Expense	SPL
Purchases	97,100		Expense	SPL
Rent expense	11,400		Expense	SPL
Sales		153,900	Income	SPL
Telephone costs	1,250		Expense	SPL
Trade receivables	11,900		Asset	SOFP
Trade payables		6,000	Liability	SOFP
Wages expense	20,600		Expense	SPL
	200,000	200,000		

Task 3.3

The trading account shows the | gross | profit for the period.

The final line of the statement of profit or loss shows the | profit or loss for the period |.

Task 3.4

Gross profit	£	446,950
Profit for the year	£	254,890

Workings

	£	£
Sales revenue		867,450
Cost of goods sold:		
Opening inventory	24,580	
Purchases	426,490	
Less: Closing inventory	(30,570)	
		420,500
Gross profit		446,950
Distribution costs		104,370
Administration costs		87,690
Profit for the year		254,890

Task 3.5

	Yes ✓	No ✓
If a business has a bank overdraft, this is a current liability.	✓	

Explanation:

If a business has a bank overdraft, this is a liability as the amount is owed to the bank. It is not a permanent loan and may need to be repaid to the bank in less than one year. Therefore it is a current liability.

Task 3.6

(a)

£	62,870

Workings

	£
Opening capital	32,570
Add: Profit for the year	67,460
Less: Drawings (35,480 + 1,680)	(37,160)
Closing capital	62,870

(b)

Drawings for the year will be a ☐ debit ☐ to the capital account in the general ledger.

Task 3.7

(a)

£	6,600

Workings

	£
Opening capital	60,100
Less: Loss for the year	(24,500)
Less: Drawings (28,100 + 900)	(29,000)
Closing capital	6,600

(b) The loss for the year will be transferred as a ☐ debit ☐ to the capital account in the general ledger.

Task 3.8

Capital account

	£		£
Loss (balancing figure)	**2,000**	Balance b/d (10,000 – 7,000)	3,000
Balance c/d (15,000 – 10,000)	5,000	Bank	4,000
	7,000		7,000

Explanation:

When the capital account is balanced, the missing figure is on the debit side of the account. As it is on the debit side, this reduces the owner's capital (what the business owes the owner) and so must be a loss for the year.

Task 3.9

Capital account

	£		£
Drawings	9,670	Balance b/d	14,690
Balance c/d	19,510	**Profit (balancing figure)**	**14,490**
	29,180		29,180

Explanation:

When the capital account is balanced, the missing figure is on the credit side of the account. As it is on the credit side, this increases the owner's capital (what the business owes the owner) and so must be a profit for the year.

Task 3.10

Capital account

	£		£
Drawings (12,300 + 560)	12,860	Balance b/d	26,450
Balance c/d	31,240	**Profit (balancing figure)**	**17,650**
	44,100		44,100

Task 3.11

Capital account

	£		£
Drawings (balancing figure)	**12,490**	Balance b/d	23,700
Balance c/d	28,610	Profit	17,400
	41,100		41,100

Task 3.12

Account name	Debit £	Credit £
Drawings	1,200	
Bank		1,200

Task 3.13

Account name	Debit £	Credit £
Drawings	800	
Purchases		800

Task 3.14

	✓
Net assets = owner's capital	
Net assets = capital + profit + drawings	✓
Net assets = capital + profit – drawings	
Assets – liabilities = capital + profit – drawings	

Explanation:

Drawings reduce capital and therefore must be deducted from capital and profit, and not added.

Task 3.15

£	17,600

Working:

	£
Opening inventory	2,000
Purchases	20,000
Less: Purchases returns	(400)
Less: Closing inventory	(4,000)
Cost of goods sold	17,600

Explanation:

Prompt payment discounts received are not included in cost of goods sold. Instead, they are added to the profit or loss for the period, after gross profit has been calculated. Therefore, they are excluded from this working.

Task 3.16

	£	£
Gross profit		X
Add:		
Less:		
Allowance for doubtful debts – adjustment	1,400	
Total expenses		X
Profit or loss for the year		X

Explanation:

The allowance for doubtful debts – adjustment is on the debit side of the trial balance. Therefore, it is an expense and reduces profit or loss for the year.

Task 3.17

	£	£
Gross profit		X
Add:		
Allowance for doubtful debts – adjustment		800
Less:		
Total expenses		X
Profit or loss for the year		X

Explanation:

The allowance for doubtful debts – adjustment is on the credit side of the trial balance. Therefore, it is other income and increases profit or loss for the year.

Task 3.18

	£	£
Sales revenue		83,400
Opening inventory	12,500	
Purchases	46,400	
Closing inventory	(11,000)	
Cost of goods sold		47,900
Gross profit		35,500
Add:		
Discounts received		880
Less:		
Discounts allowed	1,680	
Miscellaneous expenses	32,220	
Total expenses		33,900
Profit or loss for the year		2,480

Task 3.19

	Cost £	Accumulated depreciation £	Carrying amount £
Non-current assets			
Equipment	60,000	12,000	48,000

Task 3.20

(a) Helm Trading

Statement of profit or loss for the year ended 30 April 20X4

	£	£
Sales revenue		369,000
Opening inventory	41,000	
Purchases	245,000	
Closing inventory	(43,500)	
Cost of goods sold		242,500
Gross profit		126,500
Add:		
Allowance for doubtful debts – adjustment		2,000
Less:		
Depreciation charges	10,250	
Discounts allowed	2,950	
Irrecoverable debts	1,700	
Miscellaneous expenses	1,500	
Rent	13,700	
Wages	52,000	
Total expenses		82,100
Profit or loss for the year		46,400

(b) Helm Trading
Statement of financial position as at 30 April 20X4

	Cost £	Accumulated depreciation £	Carrying amount £
Non-current assets			
Furniture and fittings	72,500	38,350	34,150
Current assets			
Inventory		43,500	
Trade receivables (60,000 – 1,200)		58,800	
Prepayments		1,500	
		103,800	
Current liabilities			
Bank overdraft	1,650		
Trade payables	40,800		
Accruals	1,000		
VAT	4,100		
		47,550	
Net current assets			56,250
Net assets			90,400
Financed by:			
Capital			
Opening capital			74,000
Add: Profit for the year (per SPL)			46,400
Less: Drawings			30,000
Closing capital			90,400

Chapter 4

Task 4.1

A partnership is a relationship between persons carrying on a business in common with a view to [profit] .

Task 4.2

Debit	Partner's current account
Credit	Bank

Task 4.3

Debit	Profit or loss appropriation account
Credit	Partner's current account

Explanation:

Interest on partners' capital reduces the share of residual profit or loss available to be allocated to the partners. Being an appropriation of profit it is a debit to the partnership appropriation account.

Since partners have earned the money through their investment in the business, their current accounts are credited with interest arising on their capital.

Task 4.4

Current account – Jim

	£		£
Drawings	58,000	Balance b/d	8,000
Balance c/d	4,000	Share of profit or loss (135,000 × 40%)	54,000
	62,000		62,000
		Balance b/d	4,000

Current account – Rob

	£		£
Balance b/d	1,000	Share of profit or loss (135,000 × 40%)	54,000
Drawings	40,000		
Balance c/d	13,000		
	54,000		54,000
		Balance b/d	13,000

Current account – Fiona

	£		£
Drawings	32,000	Balance b/d	6,500
Balance c/d	1,500	Share of profit or loss (135,000 × 20%)	27,000
	33,500		33,500
		Balance b/d	1,500

Task 4.5

Capital accounts

	Ian £	Max £	Len £		Ian £	Max £	Len £
Goodwill (£18,000 × 40%:40%: 20%)	7,200	7,200	3,600	Balance b/d	85,000	60,000	
Balance c/d	88,600	60,000	29,000	Goodwill (£18,000 × 60%:40%)	10,800	7,200	
				Bank			32,600
	95,800	67,200	32,600		95,800	67,200	32,600

Task 4.6

(a) Capital accounts

	Theo £	Deb £	Fran £		Theo £	Deb £	Fran £
Goodwill (£54,000 × 75%:25%)	40,500		13,500	Balance b/d	84,000	62,000	37,000
Bank		10,000		Current accounts		1,300	
Loan (balancing figure)		69,500		Goodwill (£54,000 × 60%:30%: 10%)	32,400	16,200	5,400
Balance c/d	75,900		28,900				
	116,400	79,500	42,400		116,400	79,500	42,400

Current accounts

	Theo £	Deb £	Fran £		Theo £	Deb £	Fran £
Capital accounts		1,300		Balance b/d	4,500	1,300	6,200
Balance c/d	4,500		6,200				
	4,500	1,300	6,200		4,500	1,300	6,200

Explanation:

Upon retirement, any money in Deb's current account will be transferred to her capital account. As is seen above, the opening balance of £1,300 in Deb's current account is moved to her capital account.

(b) When a partner retires from a partnership business, the balance on the

| partner's | | current account | must be transferred to the

| partner's capital account | .

Task 4.7

(a) Partnership appropriation account for the year ended 30 June 20X8

	£	
Profit for appropriation	39,950	
Salary – Josh	0	
Salary – Ken (£500 × 12)	–6,000	Enter any deductions as negative eg –999
Sales commission – Josh	–800	
Sales commission – Ken	–2,500	
Interest on capital – Josh	–400	
Interest on capital – Ken	–250	
Residual profit available for distribution	30,000	
Share of residual profit or loss:		
Share of profit or loss – Josh (30,000 × 70%)	21,000	
Share of profit or loss – Ken (30,000 × 30%)	9,000	
Total residual profit or loss distributed	30,000	

(b)

Current account – Josh

	£		£
Drawings	20,000	Balance b/d	1,300
Balance c/d	3,500	Sales commission	800
		Interest on capital	400
		Share of profit or loss	21,000
	23,500		23,500
		Balance b/d	3,500

Current account – Ken

	£		£
Drawings	17,400	Balance b/d	800
Balance c/d	1,150	Salary	6,000
		Sales commission	2,500
		Interest on capital	250
		Share of profit or loss	9,000
	18,550		18,550
		Balance b/d	1,150

Task 4.8

Capital account – Fabio

	£		£
Goodwill (£44,000 × 20%)	8,800	Balance b/d	0
Balance c/d	51,200	Bank	60,000
	60,000		60,000

Task 4.9

(a) Madison Partnership
Statement of profit or loss for the year ended 31 July 20X4

	£	£
Sales revenue		265,550
Opening inventory	13,300	
Purchases	186,410	
Closing inventory	–9,000	
Cost of goods sold		190,710
Gross profit		74,840
Add:		
Bank interest		50
Less:		
Advertising	4,940	
Allowance for doubtful debts – adjustment	1,500	
Depreciation charges	11,080	
Office expenses	2,400	
Payroll expenses	5,100	
Total expenses		25,020
Profit/loss for the year		49,870

(b)

	£
Jo – share of profit or loss (49,870 x 50%)	24,935
Emily – share of profit or loss (49,870 x 50%)	24,935

(c)

	£
Jo – final current account balance (Per TB 1,000 – drawings 12,000 + profit 24,935)	13,935
Emily – final current account balance (Per TB 600 – drawings 20,000 + profit 24,935)	5,535

(d) Maddison Partnership

Statement of financial position as at 31 July 20X4

	Cost £	Accumulated depreciation £	Carrying amount £
Non-current assets			
Furniture	50,500	15,400	35,100
Current assets			
Inventory		9,000	
Trade receivables (55,000 – 1,500)		53,500	
Prepayments		950	
Bank		5,820	
		69,270	
Current liabilities			
Accruals	400		
Trade payables	33,100		
VAT	1,400		
		34,900	
Net current assets			34,370
Net assets			69,470

Financed by:	Jo	Emily	Total
Capital accounts	30,000	20,000	50,000
Current accounts	13,935	5,535	19,470
	43,935	25,535	69,470

Chapter 5

Task 5.1

Reason for their interest in the final accounts	User groups
View the accounts with the objective of assessing the tax payable by the organisation	Tax authorities
View the accounts with the objective of understanding the organisation's ability to pay its debts	Credit suppliers
View the accounts as the organisation affects them in many ways (eg by providing jobs and using local suppliers, or by affecting the environment)	The public
View the accounts with a view to assessing the current daily activities of the company, to assist with planning decisions	Management

Task 5.2

	✓
So that accurate information is submitted to the taxation authority	
So that users are able to understand the financial statements and compare them year on year and from one company to another	✓
So that investors can see the difference in working capital between a manufacturing company and a service provider	
To remove any differences between companies that are funded through loan capital as opposed to those that are funded through a public listing	

Explanation:

With increased globalisation and cross-listing on the world's capital markets, if financial information from different companies cannot be **compared**, it significantly reduces its usefulness.

In addition, users will be knowledgeable of the accounting standards and so when companies obey the standards, users will be able to **understand** them.

Task 5.3

	✓
Companies Act 2006	
Charities Act 2011	
International Accounting Standard 1 (IAS 1)	
International Accounting Standards Board	✓

Explanation:

The International Accounting Standards Board (IASB) is responsible for issuing International Financial Reporting Standards (IFRS).

Task 5.4

	✓
Companies Act 2006	
Charities Act 2011	
International Accounting Standard 1 (IAS 1)	✓
International Accounting Standards Board	

Explanation:

International Accounting Standard 1 (IAS 1) sets out the presentation of general purpose financial statements in accordance with IFRSs. A complete set of financial statements includes a statement of profit or loss and a statement of financial position.

Task 5.5

Sole traders	
Partnership (unincorporated)	
Limited liability partnership	✓
Limited company	✓

Explanation:

The Companies Act 2006 applies to all incorporated UK companies. It does not apply to non-UK companies or unincorporated entities (for example, sole traders).

Limited liability partnerships must follow many provisions of the Companies Act 2006 although not all.

Task 5.6

	✓
To ensure compliance with the Companies Act 2006.	✓
To maximise shareholder wealth.	
To enable the company to pay tax as it falls due to the tax authorities.	
To demonstrate a strong statement of financial position.	
To ensure compliance with International Financial Reporting Standards.	✓

Task 5.7

Financial statements for limited companies must be prepared at least | annually | and filed at Companies House.

Task 5.8

	Answer
The Companies Act states that notes must be provided as part of the financial statements of a company.	True
The Companies Act states that notes must be provided as part of the accounts for a sole trader.	False

Explanation:

The provisions of the Companies Act must be applied by limited companies. They do not apply to unincorporated organisations such as sole traders.

Task 5.9

Primary users
Existing and potential investors
Lenders and other creditors

Explanation:

According to the *Conceptual Framework* the objective of financial reporting is 'to provide financial information about the reporting entity that is useful to existing and potential investors, lenders and other creditors in making decisions about providing resources to the entity'.

Task 5.10

An employee may require information from a set of limited company accounts to

assess the company's ability to pay out pensions in the future .

Explanation:

Employees have a vested interest in whether the company will be profitable in the future and whether it has good long-term growth prospects. These factors have a direct effect on whether the company will be able to pay out pensions when the employee reaches retirement age.

Task 5.11

	✓
IAS 1	
IAS 2	
IAS 6	
IAS 16	✓

Explanation:

IAS 16 *Property, Plant and Equipment* provides guidance on accounting for property, plant and equipment.

Task 5.12

	✓
IAS 1	
IAS 2	✓
IAS 6	
IAS 16	

Explanation:

IAS 2 *Inventories* provides guidance on accounting for inventories.

Task 5.13

	✓
Comparability	
Going concern	✓
Faithful representation	
Relevance	

Explanation:

The *Conceptual Framework* mentions going concern as the underlying assumption normally applied when preparing financial statements. However, it is not one of the six qualitative characteristics (relevance, faithful representation, comparability, verifiability, timeliness and understandability).

Task 5.14

Description	Underlying Assumption
The effect of transactions and other events are recognised when they occur and are reported in the period to which they relate.	Accruals
The financial statements are normally prepared on the assumption that an entity will continue in operation for the foreseeable future.	Going concern

Task 5.15

Going concern

Explanation:

Final accounts are normally prepared on the basis that the organisation will continue for the foreseeable future.

Here, this does not apply as the business is ceasing trading. Therefore, assets must be written down to the amount that they can be sold for in an immediate sale and liabilities shown at the amount they will be settled at.

Task 5.16

The Conceptual framework identifies two fundamental qualitative characteristics of useful financial information. They are relevance and faithful representation .

Task 5.17

Characteristics	✓
Neutral	✓
Confirmatory value	
Clear, concise information	
Free from error	✓
Complete	✓
Available to decision makers in time to be capable of influencing their decisions	

Task 5.18

Characteristics	✓
Assures users that information faithfully represents the economic phenomenon it purports to represent	
Confirmatory value	✓
Classifying, characterising and presenting information clearly and concisely.	
Free from error	
Predictive value	✓
Available to decision makers in time to be capable of influencing their decisions	

Task 5.19

| Comparability |

Explanation

A qualitative characteristic of the *Conceptual Framework* is that it must be possible to compare the results of different entities or to compare the results of an entity from one year to the next.

Task 5.20

| Materiality |

Explanation

Information is defined as material by the *Conceptual Framework* if 'omitting it or misstating it could influence decisions that users make on the basis of financial information about a specific reporting entity'. Here this error is clearly material because correcting it would be likely to reverse the bank's decision to lend.

Task 5.21

(a)

	True	False
Expenses for a partnership are classified into three separate groups, namely cost of goods sold, admin expenses and distribution expenses.		✓
The taxation expense must be separately disclosed on the face of a company's statement of profit or loss.	✓	
The equity interest in a limited company is presented as share capital on the face of the statement of financial position.		✓

Explanation:

Expenses for a **company** are classified into three separate groups.

Taxation is always separately disclosed. A company has a taxation expense as it is a separate legal entity, whereas the sole trader and partnership are not legal entities and therefore do not pay tax in their own right. The sole trader and partners pay tax on the business profit.

The equity interest of a limited company is split between share capital and different reserves such as retained earnings and share premium.

(b)

	✓
There is more than one owner in a company so responsibility for running the business will be split.	
Running a company is less costly than running a partnership due to the is tighter regulation and standards that a company must obey.	
A partnership does not need to produce year-end financial statements.	
A public company can easily raise additional capital finance on the open market, through selling shares.	✓

Explanation:

There is more than one owner in a partnership as well as in a company.

Running a company is **more expensive** than running a partnership due to the additional regulations.

All businesses must also produce year-end financial statements, not just companies.

Should companies require additional finance, they may list additional shares on the open market, if they are public companies.

(c)

	✓
The non-current liabilities of a company are limited to a certain amount.	
The shareholders of a company have joint and severable liability, in the case of liquidation.	
In the case of liquidation, the shareholder's liability is limited to the value of their investment.	✓
The partners in a limited liability partnership have unlimited liability in the case of liquidation.	

Explanation:

"Limited liability" has nothing to do with the liabilities of the company. It is about the owners personal liability, should the business run into financial difficulty.

The partners in a normal partnership have joint and severable liability in the case of liquidation. This means that they are jointly responsible for settling the partnership's debts.

Shareholders will lose their investment in a company if it goes into liquidation, however the creditors may not pursue the shareholders in their personal capacity.

Limited liability partnerships offer limited liability to the partners in the same way that a company offers limited liability to its shareholders, in the case of liquidation.

AAT AQ2016 SAMPLE ASSESSMENT 1 FINAL ACCOUNTS PREPARATION

Time allowed: 2 hours

Final Accounts Preparation
AAT sample assessment 1

Task 1 (15 marks)

This task is about reconstructing general ledger accounts.

You are working on the accounting records of a sole trader for the year ended 31 March 20X7. The business is VAT registered.

You have the following information:

Daybook summaries	Goods £	VAT £	Total £
Sales	159,100	31,820	190,920
Sales returns	1,610	322	1,932
Purchases	124,940	24,408	149,348
Purchases returns	None		

Further information:	Net £	VAT £	Total £
General expenses	7,510	1,502	9,012

Balances as at:	31 March 20X6 £	31 March 20X7 £
Trade receivables	17,360	18,940
Trade payables	13,345	14,656
Closing inventory	10,520	11,300
VAT	1,806 credit	Not available
Bank	3,811 debit	Not available

- General expenses are not processed through the purchases daybook.
  £9,012 was posted to the general expenses account.
  All the VAT on these expenses is recoverable.

- Cash sales of £4,200 were made, excluding VAT at 20%
  The total banked was posted to the cash sales account.

- All purchases are on credit terms.
- The trader took advantage of prompt payment discounts whenever offered. VAT has been correctly accounted for.

Receipts and payments recorded in the bank account	£
Amounts from credit customers	187,408
Amounts to suppliers	145,137
Amounts banked from cash sales	5,040
Loan receipt	8,000
Rent paid	6,900
General expenses	9,012
HMRC for VAT – payment	6,169
Drawings	23,000
Wages	15,500

(a) Find the missing discounts figure by preparing the purchases ledger control account for the year ended 31 March 20X7.

Purchases ledger control account

	£		£
▼		▼	
▼		▼	
▼		▼	
▼		▼	
	0		0

Drop-down list:

Balance b/d
Balance c/d
Bank
Cash purchases
Cash sales
Discounts allowed
Discounts received
Drawings
General ledger
Inventory
Loan
Purchases daybook
Rent
Sales daybook
Sales returns daybook
Wages

(b) **Find the closing balance on the VAT control account for the year ended 31 March 20X7.**

Note. **The business is not charged VAT on its rent.**

VAT control

	£		£
▼		▼	
▼		▼	
▼		▼	
▼		▼	
▼		▼	
▼		▼	
	0		0

Drop-down list:

Balance b/d
Balance c/d
Bank
Cash sales
Discounts allowed
Discounts received
Drawings
General expenses
General ledger
Inventory
Loan
Purchases daybook
Rent
Sales daybook
Sales returns daybook
Wages

The totals recorded in the cash book for the year ended 31 March 20X7 were:

Receipts   £200,448
Payments   £205,718

(c) **Assuming there are no year-end adjustments, what will be the opening bank account balance in the general ledger as at 1 April 20X7?**

£			▼

Drop-down list:

Debit118
Credit

....

Task 2 (15 marks)

This task is about incomplete records and applying ethical principles when preparing final accounts.

(a) **Show whether the following is TRUE or FALSE.**

Gross sales margin percentage may be calculated as: $\dfrac{\text{Gross profit}}{\text{Sales}} \times 100\%$

	✓
True	
False	

You are a trainee accounting technician who prepares final accounts for a number of sole trader clients.

You have the following information about a business for its year ended 31 March 20X7.

- It is not registered for VAT.
- The trader operates with a gross sales margin of 25%.
- Inventory at 1 April 20X6 was £5,050.
- Sales of £64,900 were made.
- Purchases were recorded as £48,390.

(b) Using this information, complete the following tasks.

(i) Calculate the cost of goods sold for the year ended 31 March 20X7.

£

(ii) Calculate the value of closing inventory.

£

You compare this figure with the results of a physical inventory count as at the year end. The total physical inventory value is £350 lower than your calculation above.

(iii) Which ONE of the following could explain this?

	✓
Some equipment used in the office was stolen during the year.	
There were unpaid sales invoices at the year end.	
A high value item was included twice in the count.	
The trader has made drawings of goods during the year.	

(iv) Update the value of closing inventory to account for the difference above.

£

The trader has a policy of allowing customers to settle their accounts one month after the sale is made.

(c) **Which of the following is most likely to be the total on the sales ledger at the end of the financial year?**

	✓
£6,940	
£16,225	
£64,900	

You are now working on the final accounts of another client.

Your manager is called away unexpectedly. He asks you to undertake a particular tasks with a deadline during his absence. You know you have not received sufficient training to do this work.

(d) **What should you do? Choose ONE.**

	✓
Do the job to the best of your ability and submit the work to the client on time.	
Ask if you may have support from elsewhere in the organisation.	
Ask a family member who is a qualified accountant to do the work for you.	
Advise the client that the deadline will be missed.	

Task 3 (18 marks)

This task is about final accounts for sole traders.

You have the following information about events on 1 January 20X7:

- A sole trader started business.

- The business was not registered for VAT.

- The sole trader transferred £13,000 of his own money to the business bank account.

- £1,100 was paid from this account for some office furniture.

- £900 of goods for resale were purchased. The supplier allowed one month of credit.

(a) **Complete the capital account as of 1 January 20X7, showing clearly the balance carried down.**

Capital

	£		£
▼		▼	
▼		▼	
▼		▼	
	0		0

Drop-down list:

Balance b/d
Balance c/d
Bank
Drawings
Office furniture at cost
Purchases
Purchases ledger control account
Sales
Sales ledger control account
Suspense

You are now working on the final accounts of another sole trader, Onyx Trading.

You are to prepare the statement of financial position for Onyx Trading as at 31 March 20X7.

- The final trial balance is below.

- A profit for the year of £42,495 has been recorded.

- Onyx has a policy of showing trade receivables net of any allowance for doubtful debts.

(b) **Using this information, complete the following tasks:**

(i) **Calculate the value of trade receivables that will appear in the statement of financial position.**

£	

(ii) **Prepare the statement of financial position for Onyx Trading as at 31 March 20X7. Do NOT use brackets, minus signs or dashes.**

Onyx Trading

Trial balance as at 31 March 20X7

	Debit £	Credit £
Accruals		1,940
Administration expenses	33,193	
Advertising expenses	2,000	
Allowance for doubtful debts		1,200
Allowance for doubtful debts – adjustment	435	
Bank	1,645	
Bank charges	280	
Capital		22,200
Closing inventory	22,420	22,420
Depreciation charges	6,150	
Disposal of non-current assets		360
Drawings	20,000	
Equipment at cost	32,800	
Equipment accumulated depreciation		14,350
Opening inventory	20,720	
Payroll expenses	10,097	
Payroll liabilities		630
Prepayments	900	
Purchases	179,250	
Purchases ledger control account		16,720
Rent	14,800	
Sales		287,340
Sales ledger control account	25,660	
Sales returns	700	
VAT		3,890
Total	371,050	371,050

Onyx Trading

Statement of financial position as at 31 March 20X7

	Cost £	Accumulated depreciation £	Carrying amount £
Non-current assets			
(1) ▼			
Current assets			
(1) ▼			
(1) ▼			
(1) ▼			
(1) ▼			
(1) ▼			
		0	
Current liabilities			
(1) ▼			
(1) ▼			
(1) ▼			
(1) ▼			
(1) ▼			
		0	
Net current assets			
Net assets			
Financed by:			
Capital			
Opening capital			
(2) ▼			
(2) ▼			
Closing capital			

Drop-down list (1):

Accruals
Bank
Bank charges
Capital
Disposals
Drawings
Equipment
Expenses
Inventory
Payroll expenses
Payroll liabilities
Prepayments
Profit for the year
Purchases
Trade payables
Trade receivables
VAT

Drop-down list (2):

Add: Drawings
Add: Profit for the year
Less: Drawings
Less: Profit for the year

(c)   Complete the following:

Drawings for the year will be transferred as a [▼] to the capital account in the general ledger.

The opening balance in the capital account on 1 April 20X7 will be:

£	

Drop-down list:

debit
credit

Task 4 (16 marks)

This task is about the knowledge and understanding underpinning final accounts preparation.

(a) **Complete the following statements:**

(i) **Which ONE of the list below is a benefit of running a business as a sole trader?**

	✓
Unlimited liability	
Limited liability	
Complete control over business decisions	
No requirement to prepare annual accounts by a certain date	

(ii) **Complete the sentence:**

A private limited company is owned by its [▼]

Drop-down list:

directors.
shareholders.
trustees.

(iii) **Which of the following businesses have owners with limited liability for its debts?**

1   The Joe and Josephine Bloggs Partnership
2   Joe and Josephine Bloggs LLP
3   Joe Bloggs plc

	✓
All of them	
3 only	
2 and 3	
1 and 2	

(iv) Complete the following:

To be a charity an organisation must satisfy the definition of a charity found in the:

▼

Drop-down list:

Charities Act.
Code of Practice for not for profit organisations.

Its purpose must be for the benefit of the | ▼ |

Drop-down list:

public.
trustees.

(b) Which ONE of the items below prescribes the format of final accounts for an organisation adopting IFRS?

	✓
IAS 1	
IAS 2	
IAS 2012	

(c) Link the boxes to match the following users of final accounts with the most likely reason for their interest. Make each selection by clicking on a box in the left column and then on one in the right column. You can remove a line by clicking on it.

User	Reason
	Assessment of the security of any loan
Management	Decision making relating to their personal investment
Shareholders	To compare information from other organisations operating within the same business sector
	To assess future performance of the business

Task 5 (15 marks)

This task is about accounting for partnerships.

(a) **Which ONE of the following should be included in a partnership agreement?**

	✓
The partnership appropriation account.	
Salaries and wages to be paid to all employees.	
The rate at which interest is to be allowed on capital.	

You have the following information about a partnership business:

> Riva, Sam and Terry have been its owners for many years.
>
> On 31 March 20X7, Riva retired from the partnership.
>
> Goodwill was valued at £52,000 and has not yet been entered in the accounting records.
>
> Profit share, effective before the retirement:
>
> Riva 50%
> Sam   40%
> Terry 10%
>
> Profit share, effective after the retirement:
>
> Sam   70%
> Terry 30%
>
> Goodwill is to be introduced into the accounting records on 31 March 20X7 with the partnership change and then immediately eliminated.

(b) **Prepare the goodwill account for the year ended 31 March 20X7, showing clearly the individual entries for the introduction and elimination of goodwill.**

Goodwill account

	£		£
▼		▼	
▼		▼	
▼		▼	
	0		0

Drop-down list:

Balance b/d
Balance c/d
Bank
Capital – Riva
Capital – Sam
Capital – Terry
Current – Riva
Current – Sam
Current – Terry
Drawings
Goodwill

You have the following information about another partnership business:

- The partners are Asma and Ben.
- The financial year ends on 31 December.
- There is no interest on capital or drawings.

Figures relating to the year ended 31 December 20X7 were as follows:

	Asma	Ben
Profit share	60%	40%
	£	£
Salary entitlement per month	1,950	1,400
Sales commission earned during the year	4,500	8,300
Drawings	28,000 over the year	2,000 each month

Profit for the year ended 31 December 20X7 was £80,000 before appropriations.

(c) **Prepare the appropriation account for the partnership for the year ended 31 December 20X7, and complete the statement below.**

You MUST enter zeros where appropriate in order to obtain full marks.

Use a minus sign for deductions or where there is a loss to be distributed.

Partnership appropriation account for the year ended 31 December 20X7

	£
Profit for appropriation	
▼	
▼	
▼	
▼	
Residual profit available for distribution	
Share of residual profit or loss:	
▼	
▼	
Total residual profit or loss distributed	

Enter any deductions as negative eg –999

Drop-down list:

Drawings – Asma
Drawings – Ben
Salary – Asma
Salary – Ben
Sales commission – Asma
Sales commission – Ben
Share of profit or loss – Asma
Share of profit or loss – Ben

On 3rd January 20X8, Ben takes some goods for personal use.

His current account will be [▼] with their value.

Drop-down list:

debited
credited

Task 6 (21 marks)

This task is about final accounts for partnerships and an introduction to reporting regulations for a limited company.

You are preparing the statement of profit or loss for the Onyx partnership for the year ended 31 March 20X7.

The partners are Jon and Pat, who share profits and losses equally. This is their only entitlement to profit.

You have the final trial balance below. All the necessary year-end adjustments have been made, except for the transfer of profit or loss to the current accounts of the partners.

(a) **Prepare the statement of profit or loss for the Onyx Partnership for the year ended 31 March 20X7.**

If necessary, use a minus sign to indicate ONLY the following:

- **The deduction of an account balance used to make up cost of goods sold**

- **A loss for the year**

Onyx Partnership

Trial balance as at 31 March 20X7

	Debit £	Credit £
Accruals		1,500
Allowance for doubtful debts		850
Allowance for doubtful debts adjustment		600
Bank	7,888	
Capital – Jon		14,000
Capital – Pat		14,000
Cash	502	
Closing inventory	25,100	25,100
Current – Jon		780
Current – Pat		390
Depreciation charges	9,700	
Furniture at cost	48,500	
Furniture accumulated depreciation		19,400
Loan interest paid	168	
Loan payable		4,000
Office expenses	31,630	
Opening inventory	24,500	
Payroll expenses	16,950	
Prepayments	1,090	

	Debit £	Credit £
Purchases	153,670	
Purchases ledger control account		21,775
Sales		255,480
Sales ledger control account	30,660	
Selling expenses	10,542	
VAT		3,025
Total	**360,900**	**360,900**

Onyx Partnership

Statement of profit or loss for the year ended 31 March 20X7

		£	£
Sales revenue			
	▼		
	▼		
	▼		
	▼		
Cost of goods sold			
Gross profit			
Add:			
	▼		
Less:			
	▼		
	▼		
	▼		
	▼		
	▼		
	▼		
Total expenses			
Profit/loss for the year			

Drop-down list:

Accruals
Accumulated depreciation
Allowance for doubtful debts adjustment
Bank
Capital accounts
Closing inventory
Current accounts
Depreciation charges
Loan interest paid
Loan payable
Office expenses
Opening inventory
Payroll expenses
Prepayments
Purchases
Purchases ledger control account
Sales ledger control account
Selling expenses
VAT

(b) Calculate Jon's share of the profit or loss for the year and his final current account balance.

Use a minus sign to indicate ONLY a loss for the year, if necessary.

	£
Jon – share of profit or loss	
Jon – final current account balance	

Where will the current account balance for Jon appear on the statement of financial position for Onyx?

Choose ONE:

	✓
Within the 'Financed by' section	
As a current liability	
His current account will not appear on the statement of financial position	

Preparation of the final accounts for a limited company at its year end requires more detailed reporting than for a sole trader or partnership.

(c) **Which of the following statements are TRUE for a limited company?**

1   A taxation charge should be shown in the statement of profit or loss.

2   A full analysis of non-current assets must appear on the face of the statement of financial position.

3   Notes to the financial statements are available to third parties.

	✓
1 and 2	
2 and 3	
1 and 3	
All of them	

AAT AQ2016 SAMPLE ASSESSMENT 1
FINAL ACCOUNTS PREPARATION

ANSWERS

Final Accounts Preparation
AAT sample assessment 1

Task 1 (15 marks)

(a) **Find the missing discounts figure by preparing the purchases ledger control account for the year ended 31 March 20X7.**

Purchases ledger control account

	£		£
Balance c/d	14,656	Balance b/d	13,345
Discounts received	2,900	Purchases daybook	149,348
Bank	145,137		
	162,693		162,693

(b) **Find the closing balance on the VAT control account for the year ended 31 March 20X7.**

VAT control

	£		£
Purchases daybook	24,408	Balance b/d	1,806
General expenses	1,502	Sales daybook	31,820
Bank	6,169	Cash sales	840
Sales returns daybook	322		
Balance c/d	2,065		
	34,466		34,466

(c) **Assuming there are no year-end adjustments, what will be the opening bank account balance in the general ledger as at 1 April 20X7?**

£	1,459		Credit

Task 2 (15 marks)

(a) Show whether the following is TRUE or FALSE.

	✓
True	✓
False	

(b) Using this information, complete the following tasks.

(i) Calculate the cost of goods sold for the year ended 31 March 20X7.

£	48,675

(ii) Calculate the value of closing inventory.

£	4,765

(iii) Which ONE of the following could explain this?

	✓
Some equipment used in the office was stolen during the year.	
There were unpaid sales invoices at the year end.	
A high value item was included twice in the count.	
The trader has made drawings of goods during the year.	✓

(iv) Update the value of closing inventory to account for the difference above.

£	4,415

(c) Which of the following is most likely to be the total on the sales ledger at the end of the financial year?

	✓
£6,940	✓
£16,225	
£64,900	

(d) **What should you do? Choose ONE.**

	✓
Do the job to the best of your ability and submit the work to the client on time.	
Ask if you may have support from elsewhere in the organisation.	✓
Ask a family member who is a qualified accountant to do the work for you.	
Advise the client that the deadline will be missed.	

Task 3 (18 marks)

(a) **Complete the capital account as of 1 January 20X7, showing clearly the balance carried down.**

Capital

	£		£
Balance c/d	13,000	Bank	13,000
	13,000		13,000

(b) **Using this information, complete the following tasks:**

(i) **Calculate the value of trade receivables that will appear in the statement of financial position.**

£	24,460

(ii) Prepare the statement of financial position for Onyx Trading as at 31 March 20X7.

Do NOT use brackets, minus signs or dashes.

Onyx Trading

Statement of financial position as at 31 March 20X7

	Cost £	Accumulated depreciation £	Carrying amount £
Non-current assets			
Equipment	32,800	14,350	18,450
Current assets			
Inventory		22,420	
Trade receivables		24,460	
Prepayments		900	
Bank		1,645	
		49,425	
Current liabilities			
Trade payables	16,720		
Accruals	1,940		
Payroll liabilities	630		
VAT	3,890		
		23,180	
Net current assets			26,245
Net assets			44,695

Financed by:	Cost £	Accumulated depreciation £	Carrying amount £
Capital			
Opening capital			22,200
Add: Profit for the year			42,495
Less: Drawings			20,000
Closing capital			44,695

(c) **Complete the following:**

Drawings for the year will be transferred as a | debit | to the capital account in the general ledger.

The opening balance in the capital account on 1 April 20X7 will be:

£ | 44,695

....

Task 4 (16 marks)

(a) **Complete the following statements:**

(i) **Which ONE of the list below is a benefit of running a business as a sole trader?**

	✓
Unlimited liability	
Limited liability	
Complete control over business decisions	✓
No requirement to prepare annual accounts by a certain date	

(ii) **Complete the sentence:**

A private limited company is owned by its | shareholders. |

(iii) **Which of the following businesses have owners with limited liability for its debts?**

1   The Joe and Josephine Bloggs Partnership
2   Joe and Josephine Bloggs LLP
3   Joe Bloggs plc

	✓
All of them	
3 only	
2 and 3	✓
1 and 2	

(iv) **Complete the following:**

To be a charity, an organisation must satisfy the definition of a charity found in the | Charities Act. |

Its purpose must be for the benefit of the | public. |

(b) **Which ONE of the items below prescribes the format of final accounts for an organisation adopting IFRS?**

	✓
IAS 1	✓
IAS 2	
IAS 2012	

(c) **Link the boxes to match the following users of final accounts with the most likely reason for their interest. Make each selection by clicking on a box in the left column and then on one in the right column. You can remove a line by clicking on it.**

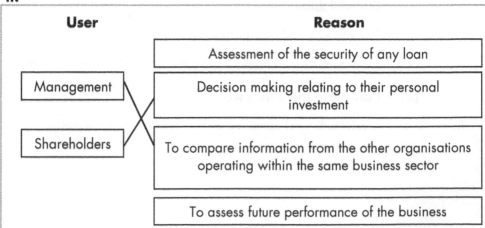

Task 5 (15 marks)

(a) **Which ONE of the following should be included in a partnership agreement?**

	✓
The partnership appropriation account.	
Salaries and wages to be paid to all employees.	
The rate at which interest is to be allowed on capital.	✓

(b) **Prepare the goodwill account for the year ended 31 March 20X7, showing clearly the individual entries for the introduction and elimination of goodwill.**

Goodwill account

	£		£
Capital – Riva	26,000	Capital – Sam	36,400
Capital – Sam	20,800	Capital – Terry	15,600
Capital – Terry	5,200		
	52,000		52,000

(c) **Prepare the appropriation account for the partnership for the year ended 31 December 20X7, and complete the statement below.**

You MUST enter zeros where appropriate in order to obtain full marks.

Use a minus sign for deductions or where there is a loss to be distributed.

Partnership appropriation account for the year ended 31 December 20X7

	£	
Profit for appropriation	80,000	
Salary – Asma	–23,400	Enter any deductions as negative eg –999
Salary – Ben	–16,800	
Sales commission – Asma	–4,500	
Sales commission – Ben	–8,300	
Residual profit available for distribution	27,000	

	£
Share of residual profit or loss:	
Share of profit or loss – Asma	16,200
Share of profit or loss – Ben	10,800
Total residual profit or loss distributed	27,000

On 3rd January 20X8, Ben takes some goods for personal use.

His current account will be ☐ debited ☐ with their value.

....

Task 6 (21 marks)

(a) **Prepare the statement of profit or loss for the Onyx Partnership for the year ended 31 March 20X7.**

If necessary, use a minus sign to indicate ONLY the following:

- **The deduction of an account balance used to make up cost of goods sold**

- **A loss for the year**

Onyx Partnership

Statement of profit or loss for the year ended 31 March 20X7

	£	£
Sales revenue		255,480
Opening inventory	24,500	
Purchases	153,670	
Closing inventory	–25,100	
Cost of goods sold		153,070
Gross profit		102,410
Add:		
Allowance for doubtful debts adjustment		600

	£	£
Less:		
Depreciation charges	9,700	
Office expenses	31,630	
Payroll expenses	16,950	
Selling expenses	10,542	
Loan interest paid	168	
Total expenses		68,990
Profit/loss for the year		34,020

(b) **Calculate Jon's share of the profit or loss for the year and his final current account balance.**

Use a minus sign to indicate ONLY a loss for the year, if necessary.

	£
Jon – share of profit or loss	17,010
Jon – final current account balance	17,790

Where will the current account balance for Jon appear on the statement of financial position for Onyx?

Choose ONE:

	✓
Within the 'Financed by' section	✓
As a current liability	
His current account will not appear on the statement of financial position	

(c) **Which of the following statements are TRUE for a limited company?**

1   A taxation charge should be shown in the statement of profit or loss.

2   A full analysis of non-current assets must appear on the face of the statement of financial position.

3   Notes to the financial statements are available to third parties.

	✓
1 and 2	
2 and 3	
1 and 3	✓
All of them	

AAT AQ2016 SAMPLE ASSESSMENT 2
FINAL ACCOUNTS PREPARATION

*You are advised to attempt sample assessment 2 online
from the AAT website. This will ensure you are
prepared for how the assessment will be presented on the
AAT's system when you attempt the real assessment. Please
access the assessment using the address below:*

https://www.aat.org.uk/training/study-support/search

BPP PRACTICE ASSESSMENT 1
FINAL ACCOUNTS PREPARATION

Time allowed: 2 hours

Final Accounts Preparation
BPP practice assessment 1

Task 1

This task is about reconstructing general ledger accounts.

You are working on the accounting records of a sole trader for the year ended 31 March 20X1. The business is not registered for VAT.

You have the following information:

Receipts and payments recorded in the bank account	£
Amounts from credit customers	109,800
Amounts to credit suppliers	58,400
Capital injection	20,000
Office expenses	30,200
Proceeds from the sale of a non-current asset	4,100
Bank charges	200

Balances as at:	31 March 20X0 £	31 March 20X1 £
Trade receivables	15,280	16,360
Trade payables	12,950	13,280
Closing inventory	12,150	13,240
Bank	13,200 credit	1,650 debit

You are also told that:

- All sales of goods are on credit terms
- A contra entry of £450 was made between the sales and purchases ledgers
- The proprietor draws £1,800 per month from the business bank account for personal use
- The proprietor transferred her own office equipment valued at £1,900 to the business during the year
- The non-current asset sold in the year was equipment

(a) **Find the total sales by preparing the sales ledger control account for the year ended 31 March 20X1.**

Sales ledger control account

	£		£
▼		▼	
▼		▼	
▼		▼	
▼		▼	

Picklist:

Balance b/d
Balance c/d
Bank
Purchases ledger control account
Sales daybook

(b) **Find the cash purchases by preparing the summarised bank account for the year ended 31 March 20X1.**

Bank

	£		£
▼		▼	
▼		▼	
▼		▼	
▼		▼	
▼		▼	
▼		▼	
▼		▼	

Picklist:

Balance b/d
Balance c/d
Bank charges
Capital
Cash purchases
Disposals of non-current assets
Drawings
Office expenses
Purchases ledger control account
Sales ledger control account

You are given the following information about a different sole trader as at 1 November 20X2:

• The value of assets and liabilities were:

	£
Non-current assets at carrying amount	17,250
Trade receivables	6,250
Bank (debit balance)	1,280
Capital	21,000

• There were no other assets or liabilities, other than trade payables.

(c) **Calculate the trade payables account balance as at 1 November 20X2.**

£	

(d) **On 30 April 20X2, cash is paid to a credit supplier, with some discount taken. Tick the boxes to show what effect this transaction will have on the balances. You must choose ONE answer for EACH line.**

Balances	Debit ✓	Credit ✓	No change ✓
Income			
Trade receivables			
Trade payables			
Bank			
Expenses			

(e) **Which TWO of the following are accurate representations of the accounting equation?**

	✓
Assets + Liabilities = Capital	
Assets − Liabilities = Capital	
Assets = Liabilities − Capital	
Assets = Liabilities + Capital	

Task 2

This task is about incomplete records and applying ethical principles when preparing final accounts.

(a) **Indicate where the accruals balance should be shown in the financial statements. Choose ONE from:**

	✓
Non-current assets	
Current assets	
Current liabilities	
Non-current liabilities	

You have the following information about a new business for the year ended 31 December 20X4:

- It is not registered for VAT.
- Sales of £45,000 were made.
- Purchases were £40,000.
- The trader operates with a mark-up of 25% on cost.

(b) (i) **Calculate the value of the cost of goods sold for the year ended 31 December 20X4.**

£ [ ]

(ii) **Calculate the value of inventory as at 31 December 20X4.**

£ [ ]

The trader rented a premises on a busy high street. Her income came only from selling goods in this store.

(c) **Taking into account the information you have, which of the following is most likely to be true for the year ended 31 December 20X4?**

	✓
Gross profit was £9,000	
Profit for the year was £9,000	

The trader took drawings from the business during the year.

Now complete the following:

The drawings [▼] recorded as an expense in the year.

Picklist:

are
are not

(d) **Which body sets global ethical standards for accountants?**

[▼]

Picklist:

Companies House
International Accounting Standards Board
International Ethics Standards Board for Accountants (IESBA)

....

Task 3

This task is about preparing final accounts for sole traders.

You are working on the final accounts of a sole trader, Martha Tidfill.

- The final trial balance is below.
- All the necessary year-end adjustments have been made.

(a) **Prepare a statement of profit or loss for the business for the year ended 31 August 20X4.**

If necessary, only use a minus sign to indicate the deduction of an account balance used to make up cost of sales.

Martha Tidfill

Trial balance as at 31 August 20X4

	Debit £	Credit £
Accruals		1,250
Bank	500	
Bank interest		2,190
Capital		20,000
Closing inventory	15,200	15,200
Depreciation charges	4,750	
Discounts allowed	1,920	
Drawings	15,000	
Heat and light	11,620	
Motor vehicles accumulated depreciation		7,600
Motor vehicles at cost	25,400	
Office costs	27,690	
Opening inventory	17,690	
Prepayments	620	
Purchases	105,280	
Purchases ledger control account		16,090
Sales		199,560
Sales ledger control account	20,150	
VAT		3,920
Wages	19,990	
	265,810	265,810

Martha Tidfill

Statement of profit or loss for the year ended 31 August 20X4

	£	£
Sales revenue		
▼		
▼		
▼		
▼		
Cost of goods sold		
Gross profit		
Add:		
▼		
Less:		
▼		
▼		
▼		
▼		
▼		
▼		
Total expenses		
Profit/loss for the year		

Picklist:

Accruals
Bank
Bank interest
Capital
Closing inventory
Depreciation charges
Discounts allowed
Drawings
Heat and light
Motor vehicles accumulated depreciation
Motor vehicles at cost
Office costs
Opening inventory
Prepayments
Purchases
Purchases ledger control account
Sales
Sales ledger control account
VAT
Wages

You have the following information about a different sole trader on 1 January 20X4:

- The sole trader started a business and transferred £8,000 of her own money into the business bank account.

- £2,000 was paid from the sole trader's personal credit card for equipment.

- Goods for resale by the business costing £1,500 were purchased from the business bank account.

(b) Complete the capital account as at 1 January 20X4, showing clearly the balance carried down.

Capital

	£		£
▼		▼	
▼		▼	
▼		▼	

Picklist:

Balance b/d
Balance c/d
Bank
Equipment
Purchases

Task 4

This task is about the knowledge and understanding underpinning final accounts preparation.

(a) **(i)** **Which ONE of the following statements is TRUE?**

1. Limited company status means that a company is only allowed to trade up to a predetermined sales revenue level in any one year.

2. For organisations that have limited company status, ownership and control are legally separate.

3. The benefit of being a sole trader is that you have no personal liability for the debts of your business.

4. Ordinary partnerships offer the same benefits as limited companies but are usually formed by professionals such as doctors and solicitors.

	✓
1	
2	
3	
4	

(ii) **Which of the following are characteristics of public limited companies?**

1. Maximising the excess of income over expenditure is not a primary objective.

2. Members can vote according to the number of shares owned.

3. Shares can be bought and sold through personal transactions of the members.

4. All members are invited to attend the annual general meeting and participate in decisions at the meeting.

	✓
2, 3 and 4	
2 and 3 only	
1 and 4 only	
3 and 4 only	

(iii) Complete the following sentence:

In a limited company it is the ultimate responsibility of the [▼] to take reasonable steps to prevent and detect fraud.

Picklist:

audit committee
board of directors
external auditor

(iv) Which ONE of the following statements about accounting information is incorrect?

1   Some companies voluntarily provide specially-prepared financial information to employees.

2   Accounting information should be relevant and faithfully represent the phenomenon it purports to represent.

3   Accountants have a strong obligation to ensure that company accounts are consistent with accounting standards.

4   Sole traders and partnerships (unincorporated) must prepare final accounts under the format prescribed by the Companies Act 2006.

	✓
1	
2	
3	
4	

(b) **Select TWO qualitative characteristics of the *Conceptual Framework.***

	✓
Going concern	
Comparability	
Accruals	
Understandability	

(c) **Which of the following groups are the owners of a limited company?**

1   Non-executive directors

2   Stakeholders

3   Shareholders

	✓
1	
2	
3	

Task 5

This task is about accounting for partnerships.

You have the following information about a partnership business:

- The financial year ends on 31 July.
- The partners at the beginning of the year were Grace, Harry and James.

	Grace	Harry	James
Profit share	40%	50%	10%
	£	£	£
Salary entitlement per year	13,200	16,800	6,000
Sales commission earned during the year	3,000	0	2,100
Interest on capital earned during the year	800	1,000	500

Profit for the year ended 31 July 20X6 was £120,000 before appropriations.

Prepare the appropriation account for the partnership for the year ended 31 July 20X6.

You MUST enter zeros where appropriate in order to obtain full marks.

Use a minus sign for deductions or where there is a loss to be distributed.

Partnership appropriation account for the year ended 31 July 20X6

	£
Profit for appropriation	
▼	
▼	
▼	
▼	
▼	
▼	
▼	
▼	
▼	
Residual profit available for distribution	
Share of residual profit or loss:	
▼	
▼	
▼	
Total residual profit or loss distributed	

Enter any deductions as negative eg –999

Picklist:

Drawings – Grace
Drawings – Harry
Drawings – James
Interest on capital – Grace
Interest on capital – Harry
Interest on capital – James
Salary – Grace
Salary – Harry
Salary – James
Sales commission – Grace
Sales commission – Harry
Sales commission – James
Share of profit or loss – Grace
Share of profit or loss – Harry
Share of profit or loss – James

Task 6

This task is about final accounts for partnerships and an introduction to reporting regulations for a limited company.

You are preparing the statement of financial position for the Jessop Partnership for the year ended 31 October 20X7.

The partners are Malcolm and Rose. Each partner is entitled to £7,250 profit share.

All the necessary year end adjustments have been made, except for the transfer of profit to the current accounts of the partners.

Before sharing profits the balances of the partners' current accounts are:

- Malcolm   £400 debit
- Rose   £230 credit

(a)   Calculate the credit balance of each partner's current account after sharing profits. Fill in the answers below.

Current account balance: Malcolm	£	
Current account balance: Rose	£	

Note. These balances will need to be transferred into the statement of financial position of the partnership which follows.

You have the following trial balance. All the necessary year-end adjustments have been made.

(b) **Prepare a statement of financial position for the partnership as at 31 October 20X7. You need to use the partners' current account balances that you have just calculated. Do NOT use brackets, minus signs or dashes.**

Jessop Partnership

Trial balance as at 31 October 20X7

	Debit £	Credit £
Accruals		970
Allowance for doubtful debts		1,280
Allowance for doubtful debts adjustment	130	
Bank		2,140
Capital – Malcolm		18,000
Capital – Rose		22,000
Cash	250	
Closing inventory	9,450	9,450
Current account – Malcolm	400	
Current account – Rose		230
Depreciation charges	2,440	
Disposal of non-current asset	2,100	
Furniture accumulated depreciation		9,240
Furniture at cost	32,980	
Marketing	17,930	
Opening inventory	21,780	
Purchases	88,810	
Purchases ledger control account		7,620
Sales		179,610
Sales ledger control account	35,090	
Wages	41,370	
VAT		2,190
Total	252,730	252,730

Jessop Partnership

Statement of financial position as at 31 October 20X7

	Cost £	Accumulated depreciation £	Carrying amount £
Non-current assets			
▼			
Current assets			
▼			
▼			
▼			
▼			
▼			
Current liabilities			
▼			
▼			
▼			
▼			
▼			
Net current assets			
Net assets			
Financed by:	Malcolm	Rose	Total
▼			
▼			

Picklist:

Accruals
Allowance for doubtful debts
Allowance for doubtful debts adjustment
Bank overdraft
Capital accounts
Cash
Current accounts
Depreciation charges
Furniture
Inventory
Marketing
Purchases
Sales
Trade payables
Trade receivables
Wages
VAT

IAS 1 *Presentation of Financial Statements* requires some items to be presented as separate line items in the financial statements and others to be disclosed in the notes.

1   Depreciation
2   Revenue
3   Closing inventories
4   Finance cost
5   Dividends

(c)   **Which TWO of the above have to be shown as line items in the statement of profit or loss, rather than in the notes to the financial statements?**

	✓
1 and 4	
3 and 5	
2 and 3	
2 and 4	

BPP PRACTICE ASSESSMENT 1
FINAL ACCOUNTS PREPARATION

ANSWERS

Final Accounts Preparation
BPP practice assessment 1

Task 1

(a) Sales ledger control account

	£		£
Balance b/d	15,280	Bank	109,800
Sales daybook (balancing figure)	**111,330**	Purchases ledger control account	450
		Balance c/d	16,360
	126,610		126,610

(b) Bank

	£		£
Sales ledger control account	109,800	Balance b/d	13,200
Capital	20,000	**Cash purchases (balancing figure)**	**8,650**
Disposal of non-current assets	4,100	Purchases ledger control account	58,400
		Office expenses	30,200
		Bank charges	200
		Drawings (1,800 × 12)	21,600
		Balance c/d	1,650
	133,900		133,900

Explanation:

The office equipment valued at £1,900 transferred to the business during the year does not affect the bank account and is therefore excluded from the ledger account above.

(c)

£	3,780

Working: 17,250 + 6,250 + 1,280 – 21,000 = 3,780

(d)

Balances	Debit ✓	Credit ✓	No change ✓
Income		✓	
Trade receivables			✓
Trade payables	✓		
Bank		✓	
Expenses			✓

(e)

	✓
Assets + Liabilities = Capital	
Assets – Liabilities = Capital	✓
Assets = Liabilities - Capital	
Assets = Liabilities + Capital	✓

Task 2

(a)

	✓
Non-current assets	
Current assets	
Current liabilities	✓
Non-current liabilities	

(b) **(i)**

£	36,000

Working: £45,000 × 100/125

(ii)

£	4,000

Working:

£40,000 – £36,000

(c)

	✓
Gross was £9,000	✓
Profit for the year was £9,000	

The drawings [are not] recorded as an expense in the year.

Explanation:

Gross profit is £9,000 (£45,000 – £36,000). The business premises are rented, and rent is an expense which will be recorded below the gross profit line but before the profit for the year. This means that the profit for the year will be lower than £9,000.

Drawings are not included as expenses in profit or loss. Instead they are recorded as a deduction in the owner's capital.

(d)

International Ethics Standards Board for Accountants (IESBA)

Task 3

(a) Martha Tidfill

Statement of profit or loss for the year ended 31 August 20X4

	£	£
Sales revenue		199,560
Opening inventory	17,690	
Purchases	105,280	
Closing inventory	–15,200	
Cost of goods sold		107,770
Gross profit		91,790
Add:		
Bank interest		2,190
Less:		
Depreciation charges	4,750	
Discounts allowed	1,920	
Heat and light	11,620	
Office costs	27,690	
Wages	19,990	
Total expenses		65,970
Profit/loss for the year		28,010

(b) **Capital**

	£		£
		Balance b/d	0
		Bank	8,000
Balance c/d	10,000	Equipment	2,000
	10,000		10,000

Explanation:

Goods for resale by the business are a purchase (included in cost of goods sold) and not a capital transaction. For this reason, the £1,500 per the scenario is excluded from the capital account.

Task 4

(a) **(i)**

	✓
1	
2	✓
3	
4	

(ii)

	✓
2, 3 and 4	✓
2 and 3 only	
1 and 4 only	
3 and 4 only	

(iii) In a limited company it is the ultimate responsibility of the board of directors to take reasonable steps to prevent and detect fraud.

(iv)

1	
2	
3	
4	✓

(b)

	✓
Going concern	
Comparability	✓
Accruals	
Understandability	✓

(c)

	✓
1	
2	
3	✓

Task 5

Partnership appropriation account for the year ended 31 July 20X6

	£
Profit for appropriation	120,000
Salary – Grace	–13,200
Salary – Harry	–16,800
Salary – James	–6,000
Sales commission – Grace	–3,000
Sales commission – Harry	0
Sales commission – James	–2,100
Interest on capital – Grace	–800
Interest on capital – Harry	–1,000
Interest on capital – James	–500
Residual profit available for distribution	76,600
Share of residual profit or loss:	
Share of profit or loss – Grace	30,640
Share of profit or loss – Harry	38,300
Share of profit or loss – James	7,660
Total residual profit or loss distributed	76,600

Enter any deductions as negative eg –999

Workings

1 Share of profit or loss – Grace: (76,600 × 40%)

2 Share of profit or loss – Harry: (76,600 × 50%)

3 Share of profit or loss – James: (76,600 × 10%)

Task 6

(a)

Current account balance: Malcolm	£	6,850
Current account balance: Rose	£	7,480

Workings

1   £7,250 – £400 = £6,850

2   £7,250 + £230 = £7,480

(b)   Jessop Partnership

Statement of financial position as at 31 October 20X7

	Cost £	Accumulated depreciation £	Carrying amount £
Non-current assets			
Furniture	32,980	9,240	23,740
Current assets			
Inventory		9,450	
Trade receivables (35,090 – 1,280)		33,810	
Cash		250	
		43,510	
Current liabilities			
Bank overdraft	2,140		
Trade payables	7,620		
Accruals	970		
VAT	2,190		
		12,920	

	Cost £	Accumulated depreciation £	Carrying amount £
Net current assets			30,590
Net assets			54,330
Financed by:	**Malcolm**	**Rose**	**Total**
Capital accounts	18,000	22,000	40,000
Current accounts	6,850	7,480	14,330
	24,850	29,480	54,330

(c)

	✓
1 and 4	
3 and 5	
2 and 3	
2 and 4	✓

BPP PRACTICE ASSESSMENT 2
FINAL ACCOUNTS PREPARATION

Time allowed: 2 hours

Final Accounts Preparation
BPP practice assessment 2

Task 1

This task is about reconstructing general ledger accounts.

You are working on the accounting records of a sole trader for the year ended 31 May 20X4. The business is VAT registered.

You have the following information:

Day-book summaries:	Goods £	VAT £	Total £
Sales	89,000	17,800	106,800
Sales returns	2,500	500	3,000
Purchases	56,000	11,200	67,200
Purchases returns	None		

Further information:	Net £	VAT £	Total £
General expenses	1,050	210	1,260

Balances as at:	31 May 20X3 £	31 May 20X4 £
Trade receivables	13,000	8,500
Trade payables	9,250	11,250
Closing inventory	3,260	4,650
VAT	555 credit	Not available
Bank	Not available	10,500 debit

- General expenses were not processed through the purchases daybook.
  £1,260 was posted to the general expenses account
  All the VAT on these expenses is recoverable.

- Cash sales of £4,000 were made, excluding VAT at 20%.
  The total banked was posted to the cash sales account.

- All purchases are on credit terms.

Receipts and payments recorded in the bank account	£
Amounts from credit customers	98,000
Amounts to credit suppliers	60,300
Amounts banked from cash sales	4,800
Loan receipt	3,000
Rent paid	6,350
General expenses	1,260
HMRC for VAT – payment	1,500
Drawings	12,000
Wages	13,000

(a) Find the missing discounts figure by preparing the purchases ledger control account for the year ended 31 May 20X4.

Purchases ledger control account

	£			£
▼			▼	
▼			▼	
▼			▼	

Picklist:

Balance b/d
Balance c/d
Bank
Cash purchases
Cash sales
Discounts allowed
Discounts received
Drawings
General expenses
Inventory
Loan
Purchases daybook
Rent
Sales daybook
Sales returns daybook
Wages

(b) **Find the closing balance on the VAT control account for the year ended 31 May 20X4.** Note. **The business is not charged VAT on its rent.**

VAT control

	£			£
▼		▼		
▼		▼		
▼		▼		
▼		▼		
▼		▼		

Picklist:

Balance b/d
Balance c/d
Bank
Capital
Cash sales
Discounts allowed
Discounts received
Drawings
General expenses
Loan
Purchases daybook
Rent
Sales daybook
Sales returns daybook
Wages

The totals recorded in the cashbook for the year ended 31 May 20X4 were:

	£
Receipts	105,800
Payments	94,410

(c) **Assuming there are no year-end adjustments, what was the opening balance in the cashbook as at 31 May 20X3?**

£		▼

Picklist:

Debit

Credit

....

Task 2

This task is about incomplete records and applying ethical principles when preparing final accounts.

On 1 January 20X8, a business had assets of £20,000 and liabilities of £14,000. By 31 December 20X8 it had assets of £30,000 and liabilities of £20,000. The owner had contributed capital of £8,000 during the year by making a payment into the business bank account. No drawings were taken during the year.

(a) **Calculate the profit or loss the business made over the year.**

£		▼

Picklist:

Profit

Loss

You are given the following information about a different business for one financial year:

Sales were £95,200 in the year, all at a mark-up of 60%. The opening inventory was £22,560 and the closing inventory was £18,420.

(b) **Using this information, complete the following tasks:**

(i) **Calculate the cost of goods sold figure for the year.**

£	

(ii) **Calculate the purchases figure for the year.**

£	

(c) **Identify whether each of the following balances is presented as a current asset, a current liability or neither on the face of the statement of financial position.**

Balances	Current asset ✓	Current liability ✓	Neither ✓
Accrual			
Opening inventory			
Prepayment			
Loan from bank payable in five years			
Bank overdraft			

You are working on the final accounts of a sole trader. The bank telephones you to ask you what the draft profit figure is because they are trying to decide whether to extend the business's overdraft limit.

(d) (i) **The ethical principal most at risk here is:**

▼

Picklist:

Confidentiality
Integrity
Objectivity
Professional behaviour
Professional competence and due care

(ii) **The action you should take is to:**

	✓
Comply with the bank's request and reveal the profit figure	
Explain to the bank that you cannot reveal the profit figure without the client's permission	
Cut off the call immediately	

Task 3

This task is about preparing final accounts for sole traders.

You have the following trial balance for a sole trader, Tom Kassam. All the necessary year-end adjustments have been made.

(a) **Prepare a statement of profit or loss for the business for the year ended 31 May 20X6.**

Tom Kassam

Trial balance as at 31 May 20X6

	Debit £	Credit £
Accruals		980
Administration expenses	12,060	
Allowance for doubtful debts		1,900
Allowance for doubtful debts adjustment		100
Bank	1,730	
Capital		12,000
Closing inventory	14,320	
Cost of goods sold	98,500	
Depreciation charges	3,880	
Discounts allowed	1,470	
Distribution expenses	25,340	
Drawings	17,790	
Furniture and fittings accumulated depreciation		6,480
Furniture and fittings at cost	24,800	
Prepayments	1,260	
Purchases ledger control account		15,940
Sales		201,560
Sales ledger control account	18,450	
VAT		2,970
Wages	22,330	
	241,930	241,930

Tom Kassam
Statement of profit or loss for the year ended 31 May 20X6

		£	£
Sales revenue			
Cost of goods sold			
Gross profit			
Add:			

Less:			
	▼		
	▼		
	▼		
	▼		
	▼		
Total expenses			
Profit/(loss) for the year			

Picklist:

Accruals
Administration expenses
Allowance for doubtful debts
Allowance for doubtful debts adjustment
Bank
Capital
Depreciation charges
Discounts allowed
Distribution expenses
Drawings
Furniture and fittings
Prepayments
Trade payables
Trade receivables
VAT
Wages

(b) Indicate where the VAT balance should be shown in the financial statements. Choose **ONE** option.

	✓
Non-current assets	
Current assets	
Current liabilities	
Non-current liabilities	

(c) Which **ONE** of the following items will appear in both the statement of profit or loss and the statement of financial position?

	✓
Drawings	
Capital	
Opening inventory	
Closing inventory	

Task 4

This task is about the knowledge and understanding underpinning final accounts preparation.

(a) **(i)** Which **ONE** of the following is a benefit of running a business as a sole trader?

	✓
No formal procedures to set up the business	
Business is highly dependent on the owner	
An absence of economies of scale	

(ii) **For which type of organisation are the terms 'equity' used to represent ownership in the statement of financial position and 'dividends' to represent amounts taken by owners? Select ONE option.**

	✓
A sole trader	
A partnership (unincorporated)	
A limited liability partnership	
A limited company	

(iii) **Which type of business does not have share capital? Select ONE option.**

	✓
A private limited company	
A public limited company	
A sole trader	

(iv) ADB is a not for profit organisation which has been set up for public benefit and is managed by its trustees.

Which ONE of the following best describes ADB?

	✓
A partnership	
A public company	
A sole trader	
A charity	

(b) **Which TWO of the following are fundamental qualitative characteristics of the *Conceptual Framework*?**

	✓
Comparability	
Understandability	
Faithful representation	
Timeliness	
Verifiability	
Relevance	

(c) **Which ONE of the following statements regarding ordinary share capital is correct?**

	✓
Dividends must be paid on ordinary share capital every financial year.	
On liquidation of the company, ordinary shares entitle the shareholder to have their capital repaid ahead of other creditors.	
Ordinary shares may or may not have voting rights attached.	

Task 5

This task is about accounting for partnerships.

You have the following information about a partnership:

The partners are Nigel and Paula.

- Gavin was admitted to the partnership on 1 June 20X7 when he paid £18,500 into the bank account.

- Profit share, effective until 31 May 20X7:

  - Nigel 25%
  - Paula 75%

- Profit share, effective from 1 June 20X7:

  - Nigel 30%
  - Paula 50%
  - Gavin 20%

- Goodwill was valued at £50,000 on 31 May 20X7 and has not yet been entered in the accounting records.

- Goodwill is to be introduced into the partners' capital accounts on 31 May 20X7 with the partnership change and then eliminated on 1 June.

(a) **Prepare the capital account for Gavin, the new partner, showing clearly the balance carried down as at 1 June 20X7.**

Capital account – Gavin

	£			£
▼		▼		
▼		▼		

Picklist:

Balance b/d
Balance c/d
Bank
Goodwill

(b) **Identify whether each of the following statements is true or false.**

	True ✓	False ✓
When a partner retires from a partnership, they must always be paid what they are owed in cash.		
In a partnership, the partners are both the owners and managers of the organisation.		

Task 6

This task is about accounting for partnerships and an introduction to reporting regulations for a limited company.

You have the following information about a partnership:

- The financial year ends on 30 September 20X5.
- The partners are William, Richard and Steve.

	William	Richard	Steve
Profit share	30%	45%	25%
	£	£	£
Salary entitlement per year	15,600	17,200	12,900
Interest on capital earned during the year	1,000	800	600
Interest on drawings taken during the year	200	100	100
Drawings for the year	22,890	51,250	17,240

After other appropriations, there is a residual profit for distribution of £72,000 for the year ended 30 September 20X5.

(a) Prepare the current accounts for the partners for the year ended 30 September 20X5. Show clearly the balances carried down.

You MUST enter zeros where appropriate in order to obtain full marks. Do NOT use brackets, minus signs or dashes.

Current accounts

	William £	Richard £	Steve £		William £	Richard £	Steve £
Balance b/d	0	1,230	950	Balance b/d	200	0	0
▼				▼			
▼				▼			
▼				▼			
▼				▼			

Picklist:

Balance c/d
Drawings
Interest on capital
Interest on drawings
Salaries
Share of profit or loss

(b) **Which of the following is the best description of fair presentation in accordance with IAS 1 *Presentation of Financial Statements*?**

	✓
The financial statements are accurate.	
The financial statements are as accurate as possible given the accounting systems of the organisation.	
The directors of the company have stated that the financial statements are accurate and correctly prepared.	
The financial statements faithfully represent the effects of transactions, other events and conditions.	

BPP PRACTICE ASSESSMENT 2
FINAL ACCOUNTS PREPARATION

ANSWERS

Final Accounts Preparation
BPP practice assessment 2

Task 1

(a) Purchases ledger control account

	£		£
Bank	60,300	Balance b/d	9,250
Discounts received (balancing figure)	**4,900**	Purchase daybook	67,200
Balance c/d	11,250		
	76,450		76,450

(b) VAT control

	£		£
Purchase daybook	11,200	Balance b/d	555
General expenses	210	Sales daybook	17,800
Bank	1,500	Cash sales (4,000 × 20%)	800
Sales returns daybook	500		
Balance c/d	**5,745**		
	19,155		19,155

(c)

£	890	Credit

Workings

£10,500 + £94,410 – £105,800

Bank

	£		£
Receipts	105,800	**Balance b/d (balancing figure)**	**890**
		Payments	94,410
		Balance c/d	10,500
	105,800		105,800

....

Task 2

(a)

£	4,000	Loss

Workings

Capital account

	£		£
Loss (balancing figure)	4,000	Balance b/d (20,000 – 14,000)	6,000
Balance c/d (30,000 – 20,000)	10,000	Bank	8,000
	14,000		14,000

(b) **(i)**

£	59,500

(ii)

£	55,360

Workings

	£	%
Sales revenue	95,200	160
Cost of goods sold (95,200 × 100/160) (W1)	59,500	100
Gross profit	35,700	60
Opening inventory	22,560	
Purchases (balancing figure)	55,360	
Closing inventory	(18,420)	
Cost of goods sold (from W1)	59,500	

(c)

Balances	Current asset ✓	Current liability ✓	Neither ✓
Accrual		✓	
Opening inventory			✓
Prepayment	✓		
Loan from bank payable in five years			✓
Bank overdraft		✓	

(d) (i)

Confidentiality

(ii)

	✓
Comply with the bank's request and reveal the profit figure	
Explain to the bank that you cannot reveal the profit figure without the client's permission	✓
Cut off the call immediately	

Explanation:

Under the AAT *Code of Professional Ethics* you are bound by the ethical principle of confidentiality which requires you not to disclose confidential information to a third party without permission from the client. Therefore, you cannot reveal the profit figure during that telephone call with the bank.

However, you should not cut off the call immediately as then you would not be complying with the Code's principle of professional behaviour.

Task 3

(a) Tom Kassam

Statement of profit or loss for the year ended 31 May 20X6

	£	£
Sales revenue		201,560
Cost of goods sold		98,500
Gross profit		103,060
Add:		
Allowance for doubtful debts adjustment		100
Less:		
Administration expenses	12,060	
Depreciation charges	3,880	
Discounts allowed	1,470	
Distribution expenses	25,340	
Wages	22,330	
Total expenses		65,080
Profit/(loss) for the year		38,080

(b)

	✓
Non-current assets	
Current assets	
Current liabilities	✓
Non-current liabilities	

(c)

	✓
Drawings	
Capital	
Opening inventory	
Closing inventory	✓

Task 4

(a) **(i)**

	✓
No formal procedures to set up the business	✓
Business is highly dependent on the owner	
An absence of economies of scale	

(ii)

	✓
A sole trader	
A partnership (unincorporated)	
A limited liability partnership	
A limited company	✓

Explanation:

Ownership for sole traders and partnerships is referred to as 'capital' and amounts taken by owners as 'drawings'.

(iii)

	✓
A private limited company	
A public limited company	
A sole trader	✓

(iv)

	✓
A partnership	
A public company	
A sole trader	
A charity	✓

(b)

	✓
Comparability	
Understandability	
Faithful representation	✓
Timeliness	
Verifiability	
Relevance	✓

Explanation:

The *Conceptual Framework* categorises the qualitative characteristics into fundamental (primary) and enhancing (secondary or supporting). Faithful representation and relevance are the two fundamental characteristics. The other four (comparability, understandability, timeliness and verifiability) are the enhancing characteristics.

(c)

	✓
Dividends must be paid on ordinary share capital every financial year.	
On liquidation of the company, ordinary shares entitle the shareholder to have their capital repaid ahead of other creditors.	
Ordinary shares may or may not have voting rights attached.	✓

Task 5

(a) Capital account – Gavin

	£		£
Goodwill (50,000 × 20%)	10,000	Balance b/d	0
Balance c/d	8,500	Bank	18,500
	18,500		18,500

(b)

	True ✓	False ✓
When a partner retires from a partnership, they must always be paid what they are owed in cash.		✓
In a partnership, the partners are both the owners and managers of the organisation.	✓	

Task 6

(a) Current accounts

	William £	Richard £	Steve £		William £	Richard £	Steve £
Balance b/d	0	1,230	950	Balance b/d	200	0	0
Interest on drawings	200	100	100	Salaries	15,600	17,200	12,900
Drawings	22,890	51,250	17,240	Interest on capital	1,000	800	600
Balance c/d	15,310	0	13,210	Share of profit or loss (72,000 × 30%; 45%; 25%)	21,600	32,400	18,000
				Balance c/d	0	2,180	0
	38,400	52,580	31,500		38,400	52,580	31,500

(b)

	✓
The financial statements are accurate.	
The financial statements are as accurate as possible given the accounting systems of the organisation.	
The directors of the company have stated that the financial statements are accurate and correctly prepared.	
The financial statements faithfully represent the effects of transactions, other events and conditions.	✓

BPP PRACTICE ASSESSMENT 3
FINAL ACCOUNTS PREPARATION

Time allowed: 2 hours

Final Accounts Preparation
BPP practice assessment 3

Task 1

This task is about reconstructing general ledger accounts.

You are working on the accounting records of a sole trader for the year ended 31 March 20X1. The business is not registered for VAT.

You have the following information:

	Balance at 31 March 20X0 £	Balance at 31 March 20X1 £
Trade receivables	39,000	27,500
Trade payables	15,600	18,950

You are also told that:

- Discounts allowed during the year amounted to £7,400.

- Discounts received were £2,610.

- A contra entry of £830 was made between the sales and purchases ledger control accounts.

- All sales were made on credit.

Bank account summary

	£		£
Balance b/d	59,150	General expenses	460
Sales ledger control account	195,240	Purchases ledger control account	84,230
Rental income	1,500	Wages	34,780
		Drawings	12,000
		Balance c/d	124,420
	255,890		255,890

(a) **Calculate the figure for sales for the year by preparing the sales ledger control account.**

Sales ledger control account

	£		£
▼		▼	
▼		▼	
▼		▼	
▼		▼	

Picklist:

Balance b/d
Balance c/d
Bank
Discounts allowed
Discounts received
Purchases
Purchases ledger control account
Sales

(b) **Calculate the figure for purchases for the year by preparing the purchases ledger control account.**

Purchases ledger control account

	£		£
▼		▼	
▼		▼	
▼		▼	
▼		▼	

Picklist:

Balance b/d
Balance c/d
Bank
Discounts allowed
Discounts received
Purchases
Sales
Sales ledger control account

Task 2

This task is about incomplete records and applying ethical principles when preparing final accounts.

A business had net assets at the start of the year of £47,390 and at the end of the year of £57,150. The business made a profit of £34,740 for the year.

(a)   Calculate the drawings made by the owner in the year.

£ [   ]

You have the following information about a business for the year ended 31 March 20X4.

Sales for the year amounted to £42,000, the opening inventory was £4,700 and purchases were £30,000. Gross profit margin is 33 1/3%.

(b)   Using this information, complete the following tasks.

    (i)   Calculate the figure for cost of goods sold.

    £ [   ]

    (ii)   Calculate the figure for closing inventory.

    £ [   ]

(c)   The proprietor takes goods that had cost the business £250 for her own personal consumption.

    Tick the boxes to show the effect of this on the accounts of the business. You must choose ONE answer for EACH line.

	Debit ✓	Credit ✓	No effect ✓
Bank			
Drawings			
Inventory			
Purchases			

Marion, a professional accountant in practice, gives Larch Ltd an opinion on the application of accounting principles to the company's specific transactions. Marion knew that she was forming her opinion on the basis of inadequate information.

(d) **In addition to integrity, state which other ONE of Marion's fundamental ethical principles is threatened by this situation.**

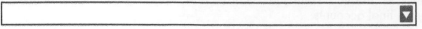 ▼

Picklist:

Confidentiality
Objectivity
Professional competence and due care

Task 3

This task is about final accounts for sole traders.

You have the following trial balance for a sole trader, Colin Woodward. All the necessary year-end adjustments have been made.

(a) **Prepare a statement of profit or loss for the business for the year ended 31 March 20X0.**

Colin Woodward

Trial balance as at 31 March 20X0

	Debit £	Credit £
Bank	2,650	
Capital		65,320
Closing inventory	13,140	
Cost of goods sold	79,470	
Depreciation charges	8,350	
Discounts allowed	260	
Disposal of non-current assets		60
Distribution expenses	3,000	
Purchases ledger control account		8,380
Rent expense	28,000	
Sales		218,400
Sales ledger control account	62,000	

	Debit £	Credit £
Vehicles accumulated depreciation		24,840
Vehicles at cost	100,000	
Wages and salaries	20,130	
	317,000	317,000

Colin Woodward
Statement of profit or loss for the year ended 31 March 20X0

	£	£
Sales revenue		
Cost of goods sold		
Gross profit		
Add:		
▼		
Less:		
▼		
▼		
▼		
▼		
▼		
Total expenses		
Profit/(loss) for the year		

Picklist:

Bank
Capital
Depreciation charges
Discounts allowed
Disposal of non-current assets
Distribution expenses
Rent expense
Trade payables
Trade receivables
Vehicles
Wages and salaries

(b) **Which ONE of the following best explains the term 'current asset'?**

	✓
An asset currently in use by a business	
Something a business has or uses, likely to be held for only a short time	
An amount owed to somebody else which is due for repayment soon	
Money which the business currently has in its bank account	

(c) **Which ONE of the following statements concerning journal entries is correct?**

	✓
Journal entries need not be authorised.	
Journal entries are used only to correct errors.	
The journal is one of the ledgers of the business.	
In the accounting records all journal entries must have a narrative explanation.	

Task 4

This task is about the knowledge and understanding underpinning final accounts preparation.

(a) **(i)** **Which ONE of the following statements regarding sole traders is correct?**

	✓
The business is legally distinct from the owner.	
All of a sole trader's profits accrue to the owner.	
Sole traders do not need to register for VAT.	

(ii) **In a company limited by shares, what is the limit of a member's liability? Select ONE option.**

	✓
The amount they guaranteed to pay in the event of the company being wound-up.	
The amount of share capital they have purchased, including any amounts outstanding on the shares that they own.	
Nothing, the company is liable for its own debts.	

(iii) A group of friends wish to set up a business. They wish to limit their liability for the business' debts to an amount that they agree to when the business is formed

Which of the following businesses is most suitable to the needs of the group?

	✓
An unlimited company	
A limited company	
A partnership (unincorporated)	
A sole trader	

(iv) **Which ONE of the following indicates that a business is being run as a sole trader?**

	✓
The business does not employ any employees.	
It does not file accounts with the Registrar of Companies.	
The business is run by one person who is not legally distinct from the business.	
The share capital of the business is not sold on a recognised stock exchange.	

(b) In applying fundamental accounting concepts the preparers of financial information are also using which of the following? Select ONE.

	✓
Legislation	
Accounting standards	
Judgement	
Financial reporting standards	

(c) For each of the following statements determine which accounting principle or concept is being invoked:

(i) Computer software, although for long-term use in the business, is charged to the statement of profit or loss when purchased as its value is small in comparison to the hardware.

Principle/concept [▼]

(ii) The non-current assets of the business are valued at their carrying amount rather than the value for which they might be sold.

Principle/concept [▼]

(iii) The expenses that the business incurs during the year are charged as expenses in the statement of profit or loss even if the amount of the expense has not yet been paid in cash.

Principle/concept [▼]

Picklist:

Accruals
Going concern
Materiality

. . . .

Task 5

This task is about accounting for partnerships.

You have the following information about a partnership.

- The financial year ends on 31 March.
- The partners are Jo, Karen and Martha.

	Jo	Karen	Martha
Profit share	60%	20%	20%
Salary entitlement per year	£45,000	£50,000	0
Sales commission earned during the year	£300	£600	£2,000
Interest on capital earned during the year	£4,400	£800	£900

Profit for the year ended 31 March 20X1 was £100,000 before appropriations.

(a) **Prepare the appropriation account for the partnership for the year ended 31 March 20X1.**

You MUST enter zeros where appropriate in order to obtain full marks.

Use a minus sign for deductions or where there is a loss to be distributed.

Partnership appropriation account for the year ended 31 March 20X1

	£
Profit for appropriation	
▼	
▼	
▼	
▼	
▼	
▼	
▼	
▼	
▼	
Residual profit or loss available for distribution	

Enter any deductions as negative eg –999

	£
Share of residual profit or loss:	
▼	
▼	
▼	
Total residual profit or loss distributed	

Picklist:

Drawings – Jo
Drawings – Karen
Drawings – Martha
Interest on capital – Jo
Interest on capital – Karen
Interest on capital – Martha
Salary – Jo
Salary – Karen
Salary – Martha
Sales commission – Jo
Sales commission – Karen
Sales commission – Martha
Share of profit or loss – Jo
Share of profit or loss – Karen
Share of profit or loss – Martha

You have the following information about another partnership business:

- The financial year ends on 31 March.
- The partners are Alex, Nicholas and William.
- The residual profit or loss to be distributed after the deduction of salaries, sales commission and interest on capital is £80,000.

	Alex	Nicholas	William
Profit share	30%	50%	20%
Salary entitlement per year	£16,500	£36,000	nil
Sales commission earned during the year	£800	£2,500	nil
Interest on capital earned during the year	£3,000	£6,000	£6,000
Drawings	£32,000	£80,000	£26,000

(b) **Prepare the current accounts for the partners for the year ended 31 March 20X1. Show clearly the balances carried down. You MUST enter zeros where appropriate in order to obtain full marks. Do NOT use brackets, minus signs or dashes.**

Current accounts

	Alex £	Nicholas £	William £		Alex £	Nicholas £	William £
Balance b/d	800	0	0	Balance b/d	0	3,000	8,600
▼				▼			
▼				▼			
▼				▼			
▼				▼			

Picklist:

Balance c/d
Drawings
Interest on capital
Salaries
Sales commission
Share of profit or loss

Task 6

This task is about final accounts for partnerships and an introduction to reporting regulations for a limited company.

You are preparing the statement of financial position for the Jasper partnership for the year ended 31 March 20X1. The partners are Aldo and Billy.

All the necessary year-end adjustments have been made, except for the transfer of profit to the current accounts of the partners.

Before sharing profits the balances of the partners' current accounts are:

* Aldo   £366 credit
* Billy   £600 credit

Each partner is entitled to £7,500 profit share.

(a) **Calculate the balance of each partner's current account after sharing profits.**

Current account balance: Aldo £ ____

Current account balance: Billy £ ____

You have the final trial balance below. All the necessary year-end adjustments have been made, except for the transfer of profit or loss to the current accounts of the partners (calculated in part a).

(b) **Prepare a statement of financial position for the partnership as at 31 March 20X1. You need to use the partners' current account balances that you have just calculated. Do NOT use brackets, minus signs or dashes.**

Jasper Partnership
Statement of financial position as at 31 March 20X1

	Debit £	Credit £
Accruals		1,190
Administration expenses	39,230	
Allowance for doubtful debts		830
Bank	4,966	
Capital – Aldo		35,000
Capital – Billy		20,000
Closing inventory	20,570	20,570
Current account – Aldo		366
Current account – Billy		600
Depreciation charges	4,525	
Disposal of non-current assets	750	
Motor vehicles at cost	43,500	
Motor vehicles accumulated depreciation		12,125
Opening inventory	23,027	
Purchases	104,250	
Purchases ledger control account		32,950
Sales		178,785

	Debit £	Credit £
Sales ledger control account	53,765	
Selling expenses	12,573	
VAT		4,740
Total	307,156	307,156

Jasper Partnership

Trial balance as at 31 March 20X1

	Cost £	Accumulated depreciation £	Carrying amount £
Non-current assets			
▼			
Current assets			
▼			
▼			
▼			
▼			
▼			
Current liabilities			
▼			
▼			
▼			
▼			
▼			

	Cost £	Accumulated depreciation £	Carrying amount £
Net current assets			
Net assets			
Financed by:	Aldo	Billy	Total
▼			
▼			

Picklist:

Accruals
Administration expenses
Allowance for doubtful debts
Bank
Capital accounts
Current accounts
Depreciation charges
Disposal of non-current assets
Inventory
Motor vehicles
Purchases
Sales
Selling expenses
Trade payables
Trade receivables
VAT

(c) **Which source provides the required formats for the statement of profit or loss and the statement of financial position for a company adopting IFRS?**

	✓
The *Conceptual Framework*	
IAS 1	
IAS 2	
IAS 16	

BPP PRACTICE ASSESSMENT 3
FINAL ACCOUNTS PREPARATION

ANSWERS

Final Accounts Preparation
BPP practice assessment 3

Task 1

(a) Sales ledger control account

	£		£
Balance b/d	39,000	Bank	195,240
Sales (balancing figure)	**191,970**	Discounts allowed	7,400
		Purchases ledger control account	830
		Balance c/d	27,500
	230,970		230,970

(b) Purchases ledger control account

	£		£
Bank	84,230	Balance b/d	15,600
Discounts received	2,610	**Purchases (balancing figure)**	**91,020**
Sales ledger control account	830		
Balance c/d	18,950		
	106,620		106,620

Task 2

(a)

£	24,980

Workings

Capital account

	£		£
Drawings (balancing figure)	**24,980**	Balance b/d	47,390
Balance c/d	57,150	Profit	34,740
	82,130		82,130

(b)   (i)

£	28,000

(ii)

£	6,700

Workings

	£	%
Sales revenue	42,000	100
Cost of goods sold (W1)	28,000	66.66
Gross profit	14,000	33.33
Opening inventory	4,700	
Purchases	30,000	
Closing inventory (balancing figure)	(6,700)	
Cost of goods sold (from W1)	28,000	

(c)

	Debit ✓	Credit ✓	No effect ✓
Bank			✓
Drawings	✓		
Inventory			✓
Purchases		✓	

(d)

Professional competence and due care

Explanation:

Marion is not acting with integrity nor is she demonstrating professional competence and due care by giving an opinion without having access to adequate information. Professional competence and due care includes acting in accordance with applicable technical and professional standards. Marion is unable to apply accounting standards without the necessary information.

Task 3

(a) Colin Woodward

Statement of profit or loss for the year ended 31 March 20X0

	£	£
Sales revenue		218,400
Cost of goods sold		79,470
Gross profit		138,930
Add:		
Disposal of non-current assets		60
Less:		
Depreciation charges	8,350	
Discounts allowed	260	
Distribution expenses	3,000	

	£	£
Rent expense	28,000	
Wages and salaries	20,130	
Total expenses		59,740
Profit/(loss) for the year		79,250

(b)

	✓
An asset currently in use by a business	
Something a business has or uses, likely to be held for only a short time	✓
An amount owed to somebody else which is due for repayment soon	
Money which the business currently has in its bank account	

(c)

	✓
Journal entries need not be authorised.	
Journal entries are used only to correct errors.	
The journal is one of the ledgers of the business.	
In the accounting records all journal entries must have a narrative explanation.	✓

Task 4

(a) (i)

	✓
The business is legally distinct from the owner.	
All of a sole trader's profits accrue to the owner.	✓
Sole traders do not need to register for VAT.	

(ii)

	✓
The amount they guaranteed to pay in the event of the company being wound-up.	
The amount of share capital they have purchased, including any amounts outstanding on the shares that they own.	✓
Nothing, the company is liable for its own debts.	

(iii)

	✓
An unlimited company	
A limited company	✓
A partnership (unincorporated)	
A sole trader	

(iv)

	✓
The business does not employ any employees.	
It does not file accounts with the Registrar of Companies.	
The business is run by one person who is not legally distinct from the business.	✓
The share capital of the business is not sold on a recognised stock exchange.	

(b)

	✓
Legislation	
Accounting standards	
Judgement	✓
Financial reporting standards	

(c) **(i)**

Principle/concept | Materiality |

(ii)

Principle/concept | Going concern |

(iii)

Principle/concept | Accruals |

Task 5

(a) **Partnership appropriation account for the year ended 31 March 20X1**

	£
Profit for appropriation	100,000
Salary – Jo	–45,000
Salary – Karen	–50,000
Salary – Martha	0
Sales commission – Jo	–300
Sales commission – Karen	–600
Sales commission – Martha	–2,000
Interest on capital – Jo	–4,400
Interest on capital – Karen	–800
Interest on capital – Martha	–900
Residual profit or loss available for distribution	–4,000

Enter any deductions as negative eg –999

Share of residual profit or loss:	
Share of profit or loss – Jo (-4,000 × 60%)	–2,400
Share of profit or loss – Karen (-4,000 × 20%)	–800
Share of profit or loss – Martha (-4,000 × 20%)	–800
Total residual profit or loss distributed	–4,000

(b)   Current accounts

	Alex £	Nicholas £	William £		Alex £	Nicholas £	William £
Balance b/d	800	0	0	Balance b/d	0	3,000	8,600
Drawings	32,000	80,000	26,000	Salaries	16,500	36,000	0
Balance c/d	11,500	7,500	4,600	Sales commission	800	2,500	0
				Interest on capital	3,000	6,000	6,000
				Share of profit or loss (80,000 × 30%; 50%; 20%)	24,000	40,000	16,000
	44,300	87,500	30,600		44,300	87,500	30,600

Task 6

(a)

Aldo	£	7,866
Billy	£	8,100

Workings

1   Aldo: £366 + £7,500
2   Billy: £600 + £7,500

(b) **Jasper Partnership**
Statement of financial position as at 31 March 20X1

	Cost £	Accumulated depreciation £	Carrying amount £
Non-current assets			
Motor vehicles	43,500	12,125	31,375
Current assets			
Inventory		20,570	
Trade receivables (53,765 – 830)		52,935	
Bank		4,966	
		78,471	
Current liabilities			
Trade payables	32,950		
VAT	4,740		
Accruals	1,190		
		38,880	
Net current assets			39,591
Net assets			70,966

Financed by:	Aldo	Billy	Total
Capital accounts	35,000	20,000	55,000
Current accounts	7,866	8,100	15,966
	42,866	28,100	70,966

(c)

	✓
The Conceptual Framework	
IAS 1	✓
IAS 2	
IAS 16	

Explanation

The *Conceptual Framework* provides the fundamental principles underlying accounting standards. IAS 2 is the standard on inventories. IAS 16 is the standard on property, plant and equipment. It is IAS 1 which provides the standard proformas for companies to use when preparing final accounts.